YALE
HEMATICAL
NOGRAPHS

6

YALE
IIVERSITY
PRESS

ALDO ANDREOTTI

Complexes of Partial Differential Operators

Yale Mathematical Monographs 6

James K. Whittemore Lectures in Mathematics
given at Yale University

Complexes of Partial Differential Operators

by ALDO ANDREOTTI

New Haven and London, Yale University Press, 1975

Published with assistance from the foundation
established in memory of Amasa Stone Mather
of the Class of 1907, Yale College.

Library of Congress catalog card number: 75-8440
International standard book number: 0-300-01887-8

Set in Times Roman type.
Printed in the United States of America by
Eastern Press, Inc.

Published in Great Britain, Europe, and Africa by
Yale University Press, Ltd., London.
Distributed in Latin America by Kaiman & Polon,
Inc., New York City; in Australasia and Southeast
Asia by John Wiley & Sons Australasia Pty. Ltd.,
Sydney; in India by UBS Publishers' Distributors Pvt.,
Ltd., Delhi; in Japan by John Weatherhill, Inc., Tokyo.

Contents

Preface

The lectures that comprise this monograph were greatly inspired by the work of Malgrange on operators with constant coefficients. I have presented a summary of some joint work with H. Grauert, C. D. Hill, S. Løjasiewicz, B. Mackichan, and M. Nacinovich (in the third chapter). The aim is to carry the classical results of the Cauchy-Riemann equations to systems of linear partial differential equations.

I am not a professional "analyst". Therefore I beg indulgence from the reader for any lack of elegance, but I have tried to be clear.

A.A.

Corvallis, Oregon
1975

1. Elementary and Levi Convexity

1. Elementary Convexity

a) We consider $\mathbf{R}^n$ as an affine space.
Let Ω be an open set in $\mathbf{R}^n$ and let $\varphi; \Omega \longrightarrow \mathbf{R}$ be a C^∞ function. At a point $a \in \Omega$ we consider the Taylor expansion of φ

$$\varphi(x) = \varphi(a) + \Sigma\partial_{x_i}\varphi(a)(x_i - a_i) + \tfrac{1}{2}\Sigma\partial_{x_i x_j}\varphi(a)(x_i - a_i)(x_j - a_j) + 0(\|x - a\|^3).$$

The quadratic form

$$H(\varphi)_a(v) = \Sigma\partial_{x_i x_j}\varphi(a)v_i v_j$$

is called the Hessian of φ at the point $a \in \Omega$.

An *affine* change of coordinates on $\mathbf{R}^n$ acts on $H(\varphi)_a$ as a linear change of coordinates

$$v \longrightarrow Av, \quad \det A \neq 0$$

and therefore the number of positive and the number of negative eigenvalues of the Hessian at a does not depend on the affine choice of coordinates in $\mathbf{R}^n$.

A function φ on Ω is called *q-convex* if at each point $a \in \Omega$ the number of strictly positive eigenvalues is $\geqslant n - q$. This notion is an affine notion.

Let $a \in \Omega$ be a point where $(d\varphi)_a = 0$. Then any differentiable change of coordinates near a acts on $H(\varphi)_a$ as the linear change of coordinates

$$v \longrightarrow J(a)v$$

where $J(a)$ is the jacobian matrix of that change of variables.

Therefore at a critical point of φ (i.e. where $d\varphi = 0$) the *signature of the Hessian is independent of the choice of differentiable local coordinates.*

b) Let Ω be an open set in $\mathbf{R}^n$ with a smooth boundary. By this we mean that there exists a C^∞ function $\varphi; \mathbf{R}^n \longrightarrow \mathbf{R}$ with the following properties;

i) $\Omega = \{x \in \mathbf{R}^n | \varphi(x) < 0\}$,
ii) at every point $x_0 \in \partial\Omega = \bar{\Omega} - \Omega$, $(d\varphi)_{x_0} \neq 0$.

James K. Whittemore Lectures, May 1974.

This means that near any point $x_0 \in \partial\Omega$, φ can be taken among a set of local differentiable coordinates so that, locally, $\bar{\Omega}$ near z_0 is diffeomorphic to a half space $\{\varphi \leqslant 0\}$. The boundary $\partial\Omega$ of Ω is given by the equation $\{\varphi = 0\}$ and the tangent space at x_0 to $\partial\Omega$ has the equation

$$\Sigma\partial_{x_i}\varphi(x_0)\, v_i = 0.$$

Let us consider the Hessian of φ restricted to the tangent space $T_{x_0}(\partial\Omega)$:

$$H(\varphi)|(v)_{T_{x_0}(\partial\Omega)} \equiv \begin{cases} \Sigma\partial_{x_i x_j}\varphi(x)_a v_i v_j \\ \\ \Sigma\partial_{x_i}\varphi(x)_a v_i = 0. \end{cases}$$

This is a quadratic form in n − 1 variables. One realizes readily that the number of negative or positive eigenvalues is independent of the choice of affine coordinates in $\mathbf{R}^n$.

Suppose that ψ is a choice of another function defining Ω as an open set with a smooth boundary. Then near any point $x_0 \in \partial\Omega$ we must have

$$\varphi = h\psi$$

where h is a C^∞ function with the property $h(x_0) > 0$.

Now

$$d.d\varphi = d.(h\, d\varphi + dh.\psi) = h\, d.d\psi + 2\, dh.d\psi + \psi\, d.dh.$$

Thus

$$H(\varphi)|_{T_{x_0}(\partial\Omega)} = h(o)H(\psi)|_{T_{x_0}(\partial\Omega)}$$

as, on $T_{x_0}(\partial\Omega)$, $d\psi = 0$ and $\psi(x_0) = 0$.

Therefore:

If Ω is an open set in $\mathbf{R}^n$ with a smooth boundary at any point $x_0 \in \partial\Omega$ the signature of the Hessian of any defining function for Ω, restricted to the tangent space at x_0 to $\partial\Omega$, has a signature which is independent of the choice of affine coordinates in $\mathbf{R}^n$ and of the choice of the defining function. Let $p(x_0)(q(x_0))$ be the number of strictly positive (strictly negative) eigenvalues of $H(\varphi)|_{T_{x_0}(\partial\Omega)}$. We must have

$$p(x_0) + q(x_0) \leqslant n - 1.$$

As an exercise one can show that there exists a disk of dimension $p = p(x_0)$ affinely imbedded in $\mathbf{R}^n$:

$$\tau : D^p \longrightarrow \mathbf{R}^n$$

(τ affine linear one to one, $D^p = \{\tau \in \mathbf{R}^p | \Sigma\tau_i^2 < 1\}$) such that

$$\tau(0) = x_0$$
$$\tau(D^p) - \{x_0\} \in \mathbf{R}^n - \bar{\Omega}.$$

Similarly there exists a disk of dimension $q = q(x_0)$

$$\tau : D^q \longrightarrow \mathbf{R}^n$$

affinely imbedded in $\mathbf{R}^n$ such that

$$\tau(0) = x_0$$
$$\tau(D^q) - \{x_0\} \subset \Omega.$$

The maximal values of p and q having these properties characterize the numbers $p(x_0)$ and $q(x_0)$ when the Hessian is nondegenerate.

c) An open set $\Omega \subset \mathbf{R}^n$ with a smooth boundary such that $\forall\, x_0 \in \partial\Omega$ we have

$$p(x_0) \geqslant n - 1 - k$$

will be called *k-convex.*

Exercise. Let Ω be k-convex and relatively compact. Show that there exists a C^∞ function φ in Ω with the following properties

i) $\forall\, c \in \mathbf{R}$ the sets

$$B_c = \{x \in \Omega | \varphi(x) < c\}$$

are relatively compact in Ω

ii) The function φ is k-convex on Ω.

Proof. (α) Let $g: \Omega \longrightarrow \mathbf{R}$ and let f be defined in an open set of $\mathbf{R}$ containing $g(\Omega)$.

Assume f, g to be C^∞ and f convex (i.e. $f' > 0, f'' > 0$). If g(x) is q-convex, so is f(g(x)). Indeed

$$ddf(g(x)) = f''_t(g(x))|dg|^2 + f'_t(g(x))\, ddg(x).$$

(β) Using this remark it follows that for $c > 0$ sufficiently large $e^{c\varphi} - 1$, where φ is a defining function for Ω, is k-convex in a neighborhood of $\partial\Omega$ in $\mathbf{R}^n$. Thus, as the function—$1/t$ is convex on $t < 0$, the function on Ω $e^{-c/\varphi}$ is a k-convex function on Ω near $\partial\Omega$ that goes to ∞ when we approach $\partial\Omega$.

(γ) Adding to $e^{-c/\varphi}$ the function $C'\Sigma x_i^2$ with $C' > 0$ and large, we get a function on Ω with the desired properties.

Remark. One could take as definition of a k-convex subset of $\mathbf{R}^n$ the properties given in the previous exercise. One obtains a definition of k-convexity that does not make use of the smoothness of the boundary nor of the fact that Ω is to be relatively compact in $\mathbf{R}^n$ (definition of "*k-convexity in the general sense*").

Example. Consider the set in $\mathbf{R}^p \times \mathbf{R}^{q+1}$, $n = p + q + 1$,

$$\Omega = \{(y, x) \in \mathbf{R}^p \times \mathbf{R}^{q+1} | \left(\sqrt{\sum_1^{q+1} x_i^2} - 1\right)^2 + \sum_1^p y_j^2 - \tfrac{1}{2} < 0\}.$$

Topologically $\Omega = D^{p+1} \times S^q$. Taking into account the geometric definitions of the invariants $p(x_0)$, $q(x_0)$ at each point $x_0 \in \partial\Omega$, one verifies that

$$p(x_0) \geqslant p \quad \forall\, x_0 \in \partial\Omega.$$

Therefore Ω is a q-convex set.
For $p = 2$, $q = 0$, Ω is a disjoint union of two balls in $\mathbf{R}^3$.
For $p = 1$, $q = 1$, Ω is a solid torus in $\mathbf{R}^3$.

d) We have the following

Theorem of Hadamard (see [12] and [13]): *If Ω is a domain* [1] *in $\mathbf{R}^n$ with a smooth boundary relatively compact and 0-convex then Ω is elementary convex (i.e. if x, y $\in \Omega$ then the segment $\{\lambda x + (1 - \lambda)y | 0 \leqslant \lambda < 1\}$ joining x and y is all contained in Ω). In particular Ω is contractible to a point and therefore*

$$H^i(\Omega, \mathbf{R}) = 0 \quad \textit{for all } i > 0.$$

If Ω is 0-convex domain in the general sense, then Ω is a union of an increasing sequence of 0-convex domains relatively compact in Ω:

$$\Omega_1 \subset \Omega_2 \subset \ldots, \Omega = \cup\, \Omega_i.$$

Indeed let $\varphi: \Omega \longrightarrow \mathbf{R}$ be a 0-convex function on Ω which is proper (i.e. $\forall\, c \in \mathbf{R}$, $\{\varphi(x) \leqslant c\}$ is compact). Select a sequence $\{c_\nu\} \in \mathbf{R}$, where c_ν is not a critical value of φ and set $\Omega'_\nu = \{x \in \Omega | \varphi(x) < c_\nu\}$. We can assume $c_1 < c_2 < c_3 < \ldots \lim c_\nu = +\infty$ so that $\Omega'_1 \subset \Omega'_2 \subset \Omega'_3 \subset \ldots$ and $\Omega = \cup\, \Omega'_i$. Each Ω_i is relatively compact with a smooth boundary. Thus Ω_i has a finite number of connected components. Let $\{K_\nu\}$ be an increasing sequence of connected compact subsets of Ω with $K_1 \subset K_2 \subset \ldots, K_i \subset \overset{0}{K}_{i+1}$, $\Omega = \cup K_i$.

Slect c_{ν_1} such that $\Omega'_{\nu_1} \supset K_1$ and set Ω_1 = connected component of K_1 in Ω'_{ν_2}. Select $c_{\nu_2} > c_{\nu_1}$ such that $\Omega'_{\nu_2} \supset K_2$ and set Ω_2 = connected component of K_2 in Ω'_{ν_2}. Continuing in this way we get the conclusion. Then we get the following

Corollary: (a) *Any 0-convex domain in the general sense in $\mathbf{R}^n$ is elementary convex.*

1. Domain means open and connected.

(b) *Any 0-convex open set* Ω *in the general sense in* $\mathbf{R}^n$ *has the property* $H^i(\Omega, \mathbf{R}) = 0$ *if* $i > 0$.

The proof of Hadamard's theorem can be obtained from the following remarks. Let Ω in $\mathbf{R}^n$ be a 0-convex domain and let $x_0 \in \partial\Omega$. We consider the Gauss map: $\partial\Omega \xrightarrow{g} S^{n-1}$ which associates to x_0 the unit exterior normal vector $\nu(x_0)$ to $\partial\Omega$ at x_0, translated to the origin. The 0-convexity assumption shows that the differentiable map g has always a nonvanishing jacobian. If $n \geqslant 3$, S^{n-1} is simply connected and g must be one to one; if $n = 2$, a direct argument establishes the same fact. Then one can show that the tangent space $T_{x_0}(\partial\Omega)$ has all of Ω on one side. Hence $\bar{\Omega}$ is an intersection of half spaces and thus it is convex. So also must be its interior Ω.[2]

From this theorem and an inspection of the example given above one is led to conjecture that

if Ω *is q-convex (or q-convex in the general sense) then one must have*

$$H^i(\Omega, \mathbf{R}) = 0 \quad \text{for } i > q.$$

e) The last conjecture can be proved by making use of standard Morse theory. One has actually the following (See [3]).

Theorem: *Let* Ω *be a q-convex open set in* $\mathbf{R}^n$ *in the general sense, then*

$$H^i(\Omega, \mathbf{Z}) = 0 \quad \text{if } i > q$$

and

$$H_q(\Omega, \mathbf{Z}) \quad \text{has no torsion.}$$

Proof. It is not restrictive to assume that we have on Ω a q-convex, proper function $\varphi: \Omega \longrightarrow \mathbf{R}$ having only nondegenerate critical points, because we can "approximate" as well as we like with first and second derivatives the given function exhibiting the q-convexity, with one having this property. At a critical point, the number of negative eigenvalues of $H(\varphi)$ cannot exceed in number $n - (n - q) = q$. Thus the index $i(p)$ of each critical point p is $\leqslant q$. Hence Ω has the homotopy type of a cellular complex with cells all of dimension $\leqslant q$. Consequently $H_i(\Omega, \mathbf{Z}) = 0$ if $i > q$, and also for the same set of i's, $H_i(\Omega, K) = 0$ where K is any field. We have also by the universal coefficent theorem

$$0 = H_{q+1}(\Omega, K) = (H_{q+1}(\Omega, \mathbf{Z}) \otimes K) \oplus \mathrm{Tor}\,(H_q(\Omega, \mathbf{Z}), K).$$

Thus $H_q(\Omega, \mathbf{Z})$ cannot have torsion.

NOTE: $H^i(\Omega, \mathbf{R}) = \mathrm{Hom}\,(H_i(\Omega, \mathbf{Z}), \mathbf{R}) = 0$ if $i > q$, as expected by the conjecture above.

2. Another proof of the theorem will be given later.

2. Levi Convexity

a) Let Ω be an open set in $\mathbf{C}^n$, $\varphi:\Omega \longrightarrow \mathbf{R}$ a C^∞ function. Using complex coordinates $z_1, \ldots, z_n$ and theirs complex conjugates, the Taylor expansion of φ at a point $a \in \Omega$ has the form

$$\begin{aligned}\varphi(z) = \varphi(a) &+ \Sigma\partial_{z_\alpha}\varphi(a)(z_\alpha - a_\alpha) + \Sigma\partial_{\bar z_\alpha}\varphi(a)(\bar z_\alpha - \bar a_\alpha) \\ &+ \tfrac{1}{2}\Sigma\partial_{z_\alpha z_\beta}\varphi(a)(z_\alpha - a_\alpha)(z_\beta - a_\beta) \\ &+ \tfrac{1}{2}\Sigma\partial_{\bar z_\alpha \bar z_\beta}\varphi(a)(\bar z_\alpha - \bar a_\alpha)(\bar z_\beta - \bar a_\beta) \\ &+ \Sigma\partial_{z_\alpha \bar z_\beta}\varphi(a)(z_\alpha - a_\alpha)(\bar z_\beta - \bar a_\beta) + 0(\|z - a\|^3).\end{aligned}$$

The hermitian quadratic form

$$\mathscr{L}(\varphi)_a(v) = \Sigma\partial_{z_\alpha \bar z_\beta}\varphi(a)\, v_\alpha \bar v_\beta$$

is called the Levi form of φ at a.

Any *biholomorphic* change of coordinates near a acts on $\mathscr{L}(\varphi)_a$ with a linear change of variables

$$v \longrightarrow J(a)v$$

where J(a) is the jacobian matrix at a of the change of variables. Thus *the number of positive and the number of negative eigenvalues of $\mathscr{L}(\varphi)_a$ does not depend on the choice of local holomorphic coordinates.*

A function φ on Ω is called *q-convex* if at each point $a \in \Omega$, $\mathscr{L}(\varphi)_a$ has at least $n - q$ strictly positive eigenvalues.

Remark. If $(d\varphi)_q \neq 0$, then one can choose new coordinates z', holomorphic near a, with $z'_1 = \Sigma\partial_{z_\alpha}\varphi(a)(z_\alpha - a_\alpha) + \frac{1}{2}\Sigma\partial_{z_\alpha z_\beta}\varphi(a)(z_\alpha - a_\alpha)(z_\beta - a_\beta)$. Then in these new coordinates the Taylor expansion of φ has the form

$$\varphi(z') = \varphi(a) + 2\mathrm{Re}\, z'_1 + \mathscr{L}(\varphi)_a(z') + 0(\|z'\|^3)$$

(so that $\mathscr{L}(\varphi)_a = H(\varphi)_a$).

b) Let Ω be an open set in $\mathbf{C}^n$ with a smooth boundary and a defining function φ. At each point $z_0 \in \partial\Omega$ one can consider the analytic tangent space $T^a_{z_0}(\partial\Omega)$:

$$\Sigma\partial_{z_\alpha}\varphi(z_0)v_\alpha = 0$$

which is the maximal linear complex subspace contained in the real tangent space. As in the case of elementary convexity we now have the following statement.

At every boundary point $x_0 \in \partial\Omega$ and for any choice of the defining function φ, the Levi form of φ restricted to the analytic tangent space to $\partial\Omega$ at x_0

$$\mathscr{L}(\varphi)\Big|_{T^a_{z_0}(\partial\Omega)}(v) \equiv \begin{cases} \Sigma \dfrac{\partial^2\varphi}{\partial z_\alpha \partial \bar{z}_\beta}(z_0) v_\alpha \bar{v}_\beta \\ \Sigma \dfrac{\partial\varphi}{\partial z_\alpha}(z_0) v_\alpha = 0 \end{cases}$$

is hermitian form in (n − 1) *variables whose signature is independent of the choice of local holomorphic coordinates near* z_0 *and of the choice of the defining function* φ.

If $p(z_0)$ is the number of strictly positive eigenvalues of $\mathscr{L}(\varphi)_{T^a_{x_0}(\partial\Omega)}$ and $q(x_0)$ the number of strictly negative eigenvalues of $\mathscr{L}(\varphi)|_{T^a_{x_0}(\partial\Omega)}$, we have

$$p(x_0) + q(x_0) \leqslant n - 1.$$

Moreover there exists an analytic disk of dimension $p = p(z_0)$;

$$\tau: D^p \longrightarrow \mathbf{C}^n$$

$D^p = \{t \in \mathbf{C}^p | \Sigma |t_i|^2 < 1\}$, τ holomorphic one to one) such that

$$\tau(0) = z_0$$
$$\tau(D^p) - \{z_0\} \subset \mathbf{C}^n - \bar{\Omega}.$$

Similarly there exists an analytic disk of dimension $q = q(z_0)$

$$\tau: D^q \longrightarrow \mathbf{C}^n$$

with

$$\tau(0) = z_0$$
$$\tau(D^q) - \{z_0\} \subset \Omega.$$

If τ is assumed to be biholomorphic, then the largest values of p and q with these properties give the geometric meaning of the invariants $p(z_0)$ and $q(z_0)$ when the Levi form is nondegenerate.

c) An open set $\Omega \subset \mathbf{C}^n$ with a smooth boundary is called *k-convex* if for every $z_0 \in \partial\Omega$ we have

$$p(z_0) \geqslant n - 1 - k.$$

More generally one can define an open set $\Omega \subset \mathbf{R}^n$ as *k-convex* if we can find a function $\varphi: \Omega \longrightarrow \mathbf{R}$ with the following properties:

i) for every $c \in \mathbf{R}$ the sets

$$B_c = \{x \in \Omega | \varphi(x) < c\}$$

are relatively compact in Ω,

ii) φ is k-convex on Ω.

One shows (with the same argument used for elementary convexity) that, if Ω is relatively compact and k-convex in the first sense, it is also k-convex in this more general sense.

Example. The set $\Omega = \{z \in \mathbf{C}^n \mid \sum_{1}^{n-k} |z_i|^2 - \sum_{n-k+1}^{n} |z_j|^2 < 1\}$ is a k-convex subset of $\mathbf{C}^n$.

d) Let us denote by $\mathcal{O}$ the sheaf of germs of holomorphic functions on $\mathbf{C}^n$. One has the following

Theorem (H. Cartan and J.P. Serre; see [9] and [25]): If Ω is a 0-convex open set of $\mathbf{C}^n$ (in the general sense),

then

$$H^i(\Omega, \mathcal{O}) = 0 \quad \text{for all } i > 0.$$

And more generally one has the following

Theorem: (see [2]), *If Ω is a q-convex open set in $\mathbf{C}^n$ (in the general sense) then*

$$H^i(\Omega, \mathcal{O}) = 0 \quad \text{for all } i > q.$$

Remark. In the previous statements the sheaf $\mathcal{O}$ can be replaced by any analytic coherent sheaf $\mathcal{F}$ defined on Ω.

The proof of these theorems can be found in any standard reference book (e.g. [9]) For the q-convex case see [2].

3. Applications of Levi Convexity

a) Open sets of holomorphy. An open set $\Omega \subset \mathbf{C}^n$ is an *open set of holomorphy* if for any divergent subsequence $\{x_\nu\} \subset \Omega$ (i.e. without accumulation points in Ω) one can find a holomorphic function on Ω with

$$\sup_\nu |f(x_\nu)| = \infty.$$

The following theorem is due to E.E. Levi ([17]).

Theorem: *Let Ω be an open set of holomorphy in $\mathbf{C}^n$ with a smooth boundary. Then for any boundary point $z_0 \in \partial\Omega$ one has*

$$q(z_0) = 0,$$

i.e. *the Levi form restricted to the analytic tangent space to $\partial\Omega$ at z_0 is positive semidefinite.*

The theorem of Cartan and Serre enables us to invert this theorem in the following form (solution of the Levi problem; see [11]).

Theorem: Let Ω be a 0-convex open set in $\mathbf{C}^n$ with a smooth boundary. Then Ω is an open set of holomorphy.

Proof. (α) Let $\{x_\nu\} \subset \Omega$ be a divergent sequence. If $\{x_\nu\}$ is divergent in $\mathbf{C}^n$ we can find a polynomial p with $\sup_\nu |p(x_\nu)| = \infty$. We can therefore assume that $\{x_\nu\}$ is bounded in $\mathbf{C}^n$ and, passing to a subsequence, that $\lim_\nu x_\nu = z_0 \in \partial\Omega$.

Let $\Omega = \{z \in \mathbf{C}^n | \varphi(z) < 0\}$, where φ is a defining function for Ω. We can find a coordinate neighborhood U of z_0 such that, on U,

$$\varphi(z) = \operatorname{Re} f + \mathscr{L}(\varphi)_{z_0}(z) + 0(\|z\|^3), \quad \text{where f is holomorphic.}$$

Thus $\{z \in U | f(z) = 0\} \cap \Omega = \emptyset$, as the Levi form is assumed to be positive definite at z_0, provided U is taken sufficiently small. Also replacing φ by $e^{c\varphi} - 1$ with $c > 0$ large, we may assume that $\mathscr{L}(\varphi)_{z_0}$ is positive definite in U (provided U is sufficiently small). Let $\varrho: U \longrightarrow \mathbf{R}$ be a C^∞ function with the properties

$$0 < \varrho(x)\ \forall\ x \in U,\ \operatorname{supp} \varrho(x) \subset U,\ \varrho(z_0) > 0.$$

Consider the function $\varphi - \varepsilon\varrho = \varphi_1$. This is 0-convex in U, if ε is small, and

$$\hat{\Omega} = \{z \in \mathbf{C}^n | \varphi_1(z) < 0\}$$

is still 0-convex with a smooth boundary. Set $V = \{z \in U | \varphi_1(z) < 0\}$ so that

$$\hat{\Omega} = \Omega \cup V.$$

(β) We make use of the *Mayer-Vietoris sequence*: Let X be a paracompact topological space and let X_1, X_2 be open sets of X such that $X = X_1 \cup X_2$. Let $\mathscr{F}$ be a sheaf of abelian groups on X. One has the following exact sequence

$$0 \longrightarrow H^0(X, \mathscr{F}) \xrightarrow{\alpha} H^0(X_1, \mathscr{F}) \oplus H^0(X_2, \mathscr{F}) \xrightarrow{\beta} H^0(X_1 \cup X_2, \mathscr{F}) \longrightarrow H^1(X, \mathscr{F}) \longrightarrow \dots$$

(here α and β are defined by the restriction maps).

If $0 \longrightarrow \mathscr{F} \longrightarrow \mathscr{C}^0 \longrightarrow \mathscr{C}^1 \longrightarrow \mathscr{C}^2 \longrightarrow \dots$ is a flabby resolution of $\mathscr{F}$ we have

$$0 \longrightarrow \Gamma(X_1, \mathscr{C}^q) \longrightarrow \Gamma(X, \mathscr{C}^q) \oplus \Gamma(X_2, \mathscr{C}^q) \longrightarrow \Gamma(X_1 \cap X_2, \mathscr{C}^q) \longrightarrow 0$$

exact with obvious definition of the maps. This gives an exact sequence of complexes whose cohomology sequence is the Mayer-Vietoris sequence.

(γ) Apply the Mayer-Vietoris sequence to $\hat{\Omega} = \Omega \cup V$ and to the sheaf $\mathcal{O}$. We get, as $H^1(\hat{\Omega}, \mathcal{O}) = 0$ by the theorem of Cartan and Serre, a short exact sequence

$$0 \longrightarrow H^0(\hat{\Omega}, \mathcal{O}) \longrightarrow H^0(\Omega, \mathcal{O}) \oplus H^0(V, \mathcal{O}) \longrightarrow H^0(\Omega \cap V, \mathcal{O}) \longrightarrow 0.$$

In particular $1/f$ is holomorphic in $\Omega \cap V$ and we can find holomorphic functions h_Ω and h_v such that

$$h_\Omega - h_v = 1/f \quad \text{on } \Omega \cap V$$

i.e.

$$h_\Omega = 1/f + h_v.$$

This shows that $\lim_\nu |h_\Omega(x_\nu)| = \infty$.

Remark. The theorem can be greatly generalized to show that an open set Ω in $\mathbf{C}^n$ with a smooth boundary satisfying the condition of Levi's theorem is actually an open set of holomorphy (solution of Levi problem).

First one shows that Levi's condition implies that Ω is 0-convex in the general sense. Then one realizes that Ω is the union of an increasing sequence of 0-convex open sets, i.e. of open sets of holomorphy. Then, by a theorem of Behnke and Stein, Ω itself must be an open set of holomorphy.

Note that to show that a 0-convex open set in the general sense is an open set of holomorphy is an immediate consequence of the theorem of Cartan and Serre for coherent sheaves (apply the theorem to the exact sequence of sheaves $0 \longrightarrow \mathscr{I} \longrightarrow \mathscr{O} \longrightarrow \prod \mathbf{C}_{x_\nu} \longrightarrow 0$ where $\mathscr{I}$ is the sheaf of germs of holomorphic functions vanishing on the points of a divergent sequence $\{x_\nu\} \subset \Omega$; $\mathscr{I}$ is a coherent sheaf).

b) By a tube-open-set in $\mathbf{C}^n = \mathbf{R}^n \oplus i\mathbf{R}^n$ we mean an open set Ω of the form

$$\Omega = \omega \times i\mathbf{R}^n,$$

where ω is an open set in $\mathbf{R}^n$.

The following theorem is elementary and due to Bochner and Martin [8].
Theorem: Let $\Omega = \omega \times i\mathbf{R}^n$ *be a connected tube in* $\mathbf{C}^n$. Ω *is an open set of holomorphy if and only if* ω *is convex* (cf. Hörmander [14], p. 41).
As a corollary one can deduce a proof of Hadamard's theorem.

Indeed let $\omega \subset \mathbf{R}^n$ be open connected with smooth boundary and 0-convex. Then $\Omega = \omega \times i\mathbf{R}^n$ is an open set of $\mathbf{C}^n$ with a smooth boundary and (as one easily verifies) Levi 0-convex. By the solution of the Levi problem, Ω is an open set of holomorphy. By the theorem of Bochner and Martin we then must have ω convex, as we wanted.

2. On the Hans Lewy Problem

1. Introduction

a) Let Ω be an open set in $\mathbf{R}^n$ with a smooth boundary $\partial\Omega$ and let us denote by $i: \partial\Omega \longrightarrow \bar{\Omega}$ the injection map.

Let us denote by $\mathscr{E}^r(\bar{\Omega})$ the space of C^∞ differential forms of degree r on $\bar{\Omega}$ (i.e. with coefficients having continuous partial derivatives of every order up to the boundary of Ω). Let us denote by $\mathscr{E}^r(\partial\Omega)$ the similar space for the manifold $\partial\Omega$.

We have a natural map

$$i^* : \mathscr{E}^{(r)}(\bar{\Omega}) \longrightarrow \mathscr{E}^{(r)}(\partial\Omega)$$

which is compatible with the operators of exterior differentiation in $\bar{\Omega}$ and in $\partial\Omega$ ($d_{\partial\Omega} i^* = i^* d_{\bar{\Omega}}$) and thus one obtains a natural map

$$(*) \qquad H^r(\bar{\Omega}, \mathbf{R}) \longrightarrow H^r(\partial\Omega, \mathbf{R}) \ \forall\, r.$$

More generally given an open set $U \subset \mathbf{R}^n$ and a C^∞ function $\varrho: U \longrightarrow \mathbf{R}$, setting $\Omega = \{x \in U \,|\, \varrho(x) \leqslant 0\}$ and assuming $d\varrho \neq 0$ on the points where $\varrho = 0$, we get for the boundary $\partial\Omega$ of $\bar{\Omega}$ in U a smooth hypersurface and a natural map (*) in cohomology.

This map is however locally trivial in the sense that we can find for every point $x_0 \in \partial\Omega$ a small connected neighborhood $U(x_0)$ such that when we replace $\bar{\Omega}$ by $\bar{\Omega} \cap U(x_0)$ and $\partial\Omega$ by $\partial\Omega \cap U(x_0)$, the map (*) reduces to $0 \longrightarrow 0$ if $r > 0$ and $\mathbf{R} \xrightarrow{\sim} \mathbf{R}$ if $r = 0$.

b) When we consider the analogous situation in $\mathbf{C}^n$ with respect to the operator $\bar{\partial}$ of exterior differentiation with respect to anti-holomorphic coordinates, the situation is much richer and not so trivial. This is what we will try to explain in the sequel. Note that now $\partial\Omega$ has no complex structure and thus the previous argument breaks down from the start.

2. The Boundary Complex

Although the situation can be described without any substantial change for a complex manifold, we will restrict our attention to open sets in $\mathbf{C}^n$.

Let U be an open set in $\mathbf{C}^n$ and let $\varrho : U \longrightarrow \mathbf{R}$ be a C^∞ function. We define

$$\begin{aligned} U^+ &= \{z \in U \mid \varrho(z) \geqslant 0\} \\ U^- &= \{z \in U \mid \varrho(z) \leqslant 0\} \\ S &= \{z \in U \mid \varrho(z) = 0\} \end{aligned}$$

and we will assume that $d\varrho \neq 0$ on S so that S is a smooth hypersurface.

On U we can consider the Dolbeault complex

$$C^0(U) = \{C^0(U) \xrightarrow{\bar\partial} C^1(U) \xrightarrow{\bar\partial} C^2(U) \xrightarrow{\bar\partial} \ldots\},$$

where $C^s(U)$ denotes the space of C^∞ exterior form of type (0, s) on U and $\bar\partial$ the usual exterior differentiation with respect to anti-holomorphic co-ordinates.

Analogously one defines the complexes $C^*(U^+)$ and $C^*(U^-)$.

Define

$$\mathscr{I}^s(U) = \{\varphi \in C^s(U) | \varphi = \varrho\alpha + \bar\partial\varrho \wedge \beta, \alpha \in C^s(U), \beta \in C^{s-1}(U)\}.$$

We have $\bar\partial \mathscr{I}^s(U) \subset \mathscr{I}^{s+1}(U)$ so that $\mathscr{I}^*(U) = \coprod_{s=0}^{\infty} \mathscr{I}^s(U)$ is a subcomplex of $C^*(U)$ (and indeed a "differential ideal"). Similarly, one defines the complexes $\mathscr{I}^*(U^\pm)$.

Finally one can consider the quotient complex

$$Q^*(S) = \{Q^0(S) \longrightarrow Q^1(S) \xrightarrow{\bar\partial_s} Q^2(S) \xrightarrow{\bar\partial_s} \ldots\}$$

defined by the exact sequence

$$0 \longrightarrow \mathscr{I}^*(U) \longrightarrow C^*(U) \longrightarrow Q^*(S) \longrightarrow 0.$$

Note that the quotient complex $Q^*(S)$ is concentrated on S and that actually, locally,

$$Q^s(S) \simeq (\mathscr{E}(S))^{\binom{n-1}{s}} \qquad (\mathscr{E}(S) = C^\infty \text{ functions on } S)$$

as one verifies taking a basis for (0, 1) forms, containing $\bar\partial\varrho$. Moreover, either by direct verification or by use of Peetre's theorem, one verifies that the operators $\bar\partial_S$ are differential operators.

It may be remarked that one can also define the quotient complex by using the complexes $C^*(U^\pm)$ and $\mathscr{I}^*(U^\pm)$, but the resulting complex is always the same.

We can thus consider four types (at least) of cohomology groups

$$\begin{aligned} H^*(U) &= \text{the cohomology of } C^*(U) \\ H^*(U^\pm) &= \text{the cohomology of } C^*(U^\pm) \\ H^*(S) &= \text{the cohomology of } Q^*(S). \end{aligned}$$

NOTE: $H^r(U) = H^r(U, \mathcal{O})$, but this is no longer true for $U^\pm$ (unless one defines on $U^\pm$ a sheaf $\mathcal{O}^\pm$ with some special behavior on S).

Remark. We have $\mathcal{I}^0(U) = \varrho C^0(U)$ so that $Q^0(S) \simeq \mathcal{E}(S)$. Then if $f \in Q^0(S)$ is the restriction of a holomorphic function on U to S, we must have $\bar\partial_S f = 0$ (tangential Cauchy-Riemann equations).

This system of equations can be also described by

$$d\tilde{f} \wedge dz_1 \wedge \ldots \wedge dz_n|_S = 0$$

where $\tilde{f}$ is any C^∞ extension of f to U. Similar interpretations hold for the other operators $\bar\partial_S$.

Example. Let $U = \mathbf{C}^2$, $z_1 = x_1 + ix_2$, $z_2 = x_3 + ix_4$, and take

$$\varrho \equiv x_4 - (x_1{}^2 + x_2{}^2) = \tfrac{1}{2i}(z_2 - \bar{z}_2) - |z_1|^2.$$

Then $S = \{\varrho = 0\}$ is the product of the paraboloid $x_4 = x_1{}^2 + x_2{}^2$ in $\mathbf{R}^3$ and the x_3 – axis.

At each point of $\mathbf{C}^2$, $d\bar{z}_1$ and $\bar\partial\varrho = -\frac{1}{2i}d\bar{z}_2 - z_1 d\bar{z}_1$ can be taken as a basis for (0, 1)-forms. Thus we get

$$Q^0(S) \simeq \mathcal{E}(S)$$
$$Q^1(S) \simeq \mathcal{E}(S) \wedge d\bar{z}_1$$
$$Q^2(S) = 0$$

so that

$$Q^*(S) \equiv \{\mathcal{E}(S) \xrightarrow{\bar\partial_S} \mathcal{E}(S) \wedge d\bar{z}_1 \longrightarrow 0\}.$$

To compute explicitly $\bar\partial_S$ we have to do the following (according to the definitions). Given $u \in \mathcal{E}(S)$ choose an extension $\tilde{u}$, C^∞ on $\mathbf{C}^2$. Evaluate $\bar\partial\tilde{u}$ and "restrict" the result to S, i.e. computing modulo $\bar\partial\varrho$ on the points of S.

We can select $\tilde{u}$ independent of x_4 so that

$$\bar\partial\tilde{u} = \left(\frac{\partial\tilde{u}}{\partial\bar{z}_1} - 2iz_1\frac{\partial\tilde{u}}{\partial x_3}\right)d\bar{z}_1 - 2i\frac{\partial\tilde{u}}{\partial\bar{z}_2}\bar\partial\varrho$$

and

$$\bar\partial_S u = \left(\frac{\partial u}{\partial\bar{z}_1} - 2iz_1\frac{\partial u}{\partial x_3}\right) \wedge d\bar{z}_1.$$

In conclusion, the complex $Q^*(S)$ is isomorphic to

$$\mathcal{E}(\mathbf{R}^3) \xrightarrow{L} \mathcal{E}(\mathbf{R}^3) \longrightarrow 0$$

where $L = \dfrac{\partial}{\partial z_1} - iz_1\dfrac{\partial}{\partial x_3}$ is the Lewy operator (on $\mathbf{R}^3 \simeq S$ when we select $z_1 = x_1 + ix_2$ and x_3 as coordinates).

3. Mayer-Vietoris Sequence

a) A C^∞ function $f \in \mathscr{E}(U)$ is called *flat on S* if it vanishes on S with all its partial derivatives. If $\mathscr{F}(U, S)$ is the space of flat functions on S, then $\mathscr{E}(U)/\mathscr{F}(U, S) = C^0(S)$ is the space of C^∞ "Whitney functions" on S. We set

$$\mathscr{F}^s(U) = \{\varphi \in C^s(U) \mid \text{the coefficients of } \varphi \text{ are flat on S}\}.$$

We have $\bar\partial\mathscr{F}^s(U) \subset \mathscr{F}^{s+1}(U)$ so that $\mathscr{F}^*(U) = \coprod_{s=0}^{\infty} \mathscr{F}^s(U)$ is a subcomplex of $C^*(U)$ and also of $\mathscr{I}^*(U)$. One can then consider the quotient complex $C^*(S)$ defined by the exact sequence

$$0 \longrightarrow \mathscr{F}^*(U) \longrightarrow C^*(U) \longrightarrow C^*(S) \longrightarrow 0.$$

Note that one has the exact sequence:

$$(1)\quad 0 \longrightarrow \frac{\mathscr{I}^*(U)}{\mathscr{F}^*(U)} \longrightarrow C^*(S) \longrightarrow Q^*(S) \longrightarrow 0.$$

This will enable us to relate the colomology of $C^*(S)$ to $H^*(S)$. One has the following lemma.

Lemma. For any choice of U and S the sequence

$$0 \longrightarrow \frac{\mathscr{I}^0(U)}{\mathscr{F}^0(U)} \xrightarrow{\bar\partial} \frac{\mathscr{I}^1(U)}{\mathscr{F}^1(U)} \xrightarrow{\bar\partial} \frac{\mathscr{I}^2(U)}{\mathscr{F}^2(U)} \xrightarrow{\bar\partial} \cdots$$

is an exact sequence.

Proof. (α) Let $u \in \mathscr{I}^0(U)$ and assume that $\bar\partial u$ is flat on S. Then $u \in \mathscr{I}^0(U)$ implies $u = \varrho\,\alpha_1$ for some $\alpha_1 \in C^0(U)$ and the assumption $\bar\partial u$ flat on S implies

$$\bar\partial\,\varrho\,\alpha_1 = 0 \text{ on S}.$$

Thus $\alpha_1 = \varrho\alpha_2$ for some $\alpha_2 \in C^0(U)$, hence $u = \varrho^2\,\alpha_2$. But then

$$\bar\partial\varrho_1 \wedge \alpha_2 = 0 \text{ on S}$$

implies $\alpha_2 = \varrho\alpha_3$ for some $\alpha_3 \in C^0(U)$ so that $u = \varrho^3\alpha_3$. In this way one show that $u = \varrho^k\alpha_k$, $\alpha_k \in C^0(U)$ for every k, thus $u \in \mathscr{F}(U)$.

(β) One makes use, to treat the general case, of the following fact.

Given on S a sequence $f_0, f_1, f_2, \ldots$ *of* C^∞ *functions there exists a* C^∞ *function F on U such that*

$$\left.\frac{\partial^k F}{\partial\varrho^k}\right|_S = f_k \quad \text{for } k = 0, 1, 2, \ldots\ .$$

Now let $f \in \mathscr{I}^s(U)$, $s \geqslant 1$, thus $f = \varrho\alpha + \bar\partial\varrho \wedge \beta$. Using the above remark one can construct $\beta_1 \in C^{s-1}(U)$ with

$$\beta_1\big|_S = \beta\big|_S$$

$$(*)\quad \left.\frac{\partial^k \beta_1}{\partial \varrho^k}\right|_S = 0 \quad \text{for } k = 1, 2, \ldots .$$

Setting $f = (f - \bar{\partial}\varrho \wedge \beta_1) + \bar{\partial}\varrho \wedge \beta_1 = \varrho\alpha_1 + \bar{\partial}\varrho \wedge \beta_1$, one realizes that every $f \in \mathscr{I}^s(U)$ can be written as

$$f = \varrho\alpha_1 + \bar{\partial}\varrho \wedge \beta_1$$

with β_1 verifying condition (*).

Let us now assume that $\bar{\partial} f$ is flat on S. Write

$$f - \bar{\partial}(\varrho\beta_1) = \varrho(\alpha_1 - \bar{\partial}\beta_1)$$

and set $\gamma_1 = \alpha_1 - \bar{\partial}\beta_1$. By the assumption we get $\bar{\partial}\varrho \wedge \gamma_1|_S = 0$, so that $\gamma_1 = \varrho\alpha_2 + \bar{\partial}\varrho \wedge \beta_2$, and we may assume β_2 verifies (*). Then

$$f - \bar{\partial}(\varrho\beta_1 + \tfrac{1}{2}\varrho^2\beta_2) = \varrho^2(\alpha_2 - \tfrac{1}{2}\bar{\partial}\beta_2).$$

Set $\gamma_2 = \alpha_2 - \frac{1}{2}\bar{\partial}\beta_2$. By the assumption $\bar{\partial}\varrho \wedge \gamma_2|_S = 0$, so that $\gamma_2 = \varrho\alpha_3 + \bar{\partial}\varrho \wedge \beta_3$, with β_3 verifying (*). Then

$$f - \bar{\partial}(\varrho\beta_1 + \tfrac{1}{2}\varrho^2\beta_2 + \tfrac{1}{3}\varrho^3\beta_3) = \varrho^3(\alpha_3 - \tfrac{1}{3}\beta_3).$$

Proceeding in this way we get a formal power series in ϱ

$$\varphi = \sum_1^\infty \frac{\varrho^{m-1}}{m}\beta_m$$

with β_m verifying (*) so that

$$f - \bar{\partial}\left(\sum_1^{m+1} \frac{\varrho^k}{k}\beta_k\right) = \varrho^{m+1}\gamma_{m+1}.$$

Using the remark at the beginning we can construct a $g \in C^{s-1}(U)$ such that

$$\left.\frac{\partial^k g}{\partial\varrho^k}\right|_S = \left.\frac{\partial^k \varphi}{\partial\varrho^k}\right|_S = \frac{k!}{k+1}\beta_{k+1} \quad \text{for } k = 0, 1, 2, \ldots .$$

Let $v = \varrho g$ then $\varrho v \in \mathscr{I}^{s-1}(U)$ and $f - \bar{\partial} v$ is flat on S.

b) One can now prove that *we do have always an exact sequence* (*Mayer-Vietoris sequence*)

$$\begin{aligned} 0 \longrightarrow H^0(U) \longrightarrow H^0(U^+) \oplus H^0(U^-) \longrightarrow H^0(S) \longrightarrow \\ \longrightarrow H^1(U) \longrightarrow H^1(U^+) \oplus H^1(U^-) \longrightarrow H^1(S) \longrightarrow \ldots . \end{aligned}$$

Proof. We have (with obvious notations) a short exact sequence

$$0 \longrightarrow C^*(U) \longrightarrow C^*(U^+) \oplus C^*(U^-) \longrightarrow C^*(S) \longrightarrow 0$$

from which we get a Mayer-Vietoris sequence with $H^*(S)$ replaced by

$H^*(C^*(S), \bar{\partial})$. But by virtue of the Lemma and exact sequence (1) we do have $H^*(C^*(S), \bar{\partial}) \simeq H^*(S)$.

c) One can replace in all considerations developed above C^∞ functions with C^∞ functions with compact support. This gives the *Mayer-Vietoris sequence with compact support*

$$0 \longrightarrow H^0_k(U) \longrightarrow H^0_k(U^+) \oplus H^0_k(U^-) \longrightarrow H^0_k(S) \longrightarrow$$
$$\longrightarrow H^1_k(U) \longrightarrow H^1_k(U^+) \oplus H^1_k(U^-) \longrightarrow H^1_k(S) \longrightarrow \dots .$$

4. Applications

a) *Extension theorems.* Let $U = \mathbf{C}^n$ and let S be a closed compact hypersurface such that $\mathbf{C}^n - S$ consists of two connected components. Let U^+ be the unbounded piece and U^- the piece bounded by S.

If $n \geqslant 2$ *then any C^∞ function f on S satisfying the compatibility conditions $\bar{\partial}_S f = 0$ is the trace on S of a function C^∞ on U^- and holomorphic on $\mathring{U}^-$*

Proof. By the Mayer-Vietoris sequence with compact supports we get an exact sequence

$$0 \longrightarrow H^0(U^-) \longrightarrow H^0(S) \longrightarrow H^1_k(\mathbf{C}^n).$$

By Serre duality $H^1_k(\mathbf{C}^n, \mathcal{O}) \simeq H^{n-1}(\mathbf{C}^n, \mathcal{O}) = 0.$

This theorem is due to Bochner, Fichera, Martinelli, and Severi (see [7] [10], [21]).

NOTE: The same argument can be applied to obtain the same theorem on any Stein manifold (or on any (n–2)-complete manifold).

b) *Equations without solutions.* Let us go back to the example above which gave us the Hans Lewy equation.

Let $a \in S$ and let U be any domain of holomorphy containing a. As $H^1(U) = 0 = H^2(U)$, we get in particular

$$H^1(S \cap U) \simeq H^1(U^+) \oplus H^1(U^-).$$

Let U be a coordinate patch, for instance, and let U^+ denote the convex piece with U^- denotes the concave piece. We make use of the following.

Lemma. Let Ω be an open subset of $\mathbf{C}^2 - \{0\}$ containing a closed half sphere

$$\Sigma = \{|z_1|^2 + |z_2|^2 = \varepsilon, \operatorname{Re} z_1 \geqslant 0\}.$$

Consider the $\bar{\partial}$ – closed, (0, 1) forms

$$\varphi_{\alpha+1} = \frac{\bar{z}_2^{\alpha_2+1}\, d\bar{z}_1^{\alpha_1+1} - \bar{z}_1^{\alpha_1+1}\, d\bar{z}_2^{\alpha_2+1}}{(|z_1|^{2(\alpha_1+1)} + |z_2|^{2(\alpha_2+1)})^2}, \alpha \in \mathbf{N}^2.$$

They define cohomology classes $\xi_\alpha \in H^1(\Omega, \mathcal{O})$ which are linearly independent.

Proof. (α) One uses the following remark. If S is any sphere centered at the origin in some open set $U \ni 0$ and if f is holomorphic on U then

$$D^\alpha f(0) = \frac{\alpha!}{(2\pi i)^2} \int_S f \varphi_\alpha \, dz_1 \, dz_2 \quad \text{(Martinelli formula).}$$

(β) Assume that $\Sigma c_\alpha \xi_\alpha = 0$. Thus $\mu \equiv \Sigma c_\alpha \varphi_\alpha = \bar{\partial}\eta$ on Ω. From the Martinelli formula applied to $S = \{\Sigma |z_i|^2 = \varepsilon\}$ we get

$$\Sigma \, c_\alpha \frac{1}{\alpha!} D^\alpha f(0) = \frac{1}{(2\pi i)^2} \int_S f \mu \, dz_1 \, dz_2 .$$

For small positive σ we can break up the integral on the right side as an integral over $S \cap \{\mathrm{Re}\, z_1 > -\sigma\}$ and an integral over $S \cap \{\mathrm{Re}\, z_1 < -\sigma\}$. The first integral, if σ is small, is extended over a surface contained in Ω. Thus by Stokes' formula we can write it as

$$\int_{\partial(S \cap \{\mathrm{Re}\, z_1 > -\sigma\})} f \eta \, dz_1 \, dz_2$$

We can find a closed rectangle Q containing

$$\partial(S \cap \{\mathrm{Re}\, z_1 > -\sigma\}) \cup (S \cap \{\mathrm{Re}\, z_1 < -\sigma\})$$

but not containing a small closed ball B centered at the origin.

Given any holomorphic function g on a neighborhood of B, we can find a sequence of entire holomorphic functions f_ν such that $f_\nu \longrightarrow g$ uniformly on B, $f_\nu \longrightarrow 0$ uniformly on Q, because $B \cup Q$ is Runge in $\mathbf{C}^2$. But then, by the previous remark, we deduce that

$$\Sigma \, c_\alpha \frac{1}{\alpha!} D^\alpha g(0) = 0$$

for every g holomorphic in B. This implies $c_\alpha = 0 \; \forall \, \alpha$.

Corollary: $\dim_{\mathbf{C}} H^1(U^-) = \infty$ (*for any coordinate ball U centered at a*).

It follows that *we can find a fundamental sequence* ω_ν, $\nu = 0, 1, 2, \ldots,$ *of neighborhoods of any point* $a \in \mathbf{R}^3$ and *for each* ν *a* C^∞ *function* $f_\nu \in \mathscr{E}(\omega_0)$ *such that the equation*

$$\frac{\partial u}{\partial \bar{z}_1} - i z_1 \frac{\partial u}{\partial x_3} = f_\nu$$

has no solution u in ω_ν.

We can improve on this statement, showing that we can find $f \in \mathscr{E}(\omega_0)$ such that the above equation has no solution u in any smaller ω_ν. This amounts to showing that *the H. Lewy complex on* $\mathbf{R}^3$

$$\mathscr{E} \xrightarrow{L} \mathscr{E} \longrightarrow 0,$$

where $\mathscr{E}$ *denotes the sheaf of germs of* C^∞ *functions, does not admit the Poincaré lemma in dimension 1 near any point* $a \in \mathbf{R}^3$.

Proof. Set $\omega = \omega_0$ and let us consider the following diagram

$$\begin{array}{ccc} \mathscr{E}(\omega) & \xrightarrow{r_\nu} & \mathscr{E}(\omega_\nu) \\ \uparrow j_\nu & & \uparrow L \\ E_\nu & \longrightarrow & \mathscr{E}(\omega_\nu) \end{array}$$

where $E_\nu = \{(\alpha, \beta) \in \mathscr{E}(\omega) \times \mathscr{E}(\omega) | r_\nu \alpha = L\beta\}$ and where r_ν denotes the restriction map. Each space $\mathscr{E}(\omega_\nu)$ has a nautral structure of a Fréchet space and the maps r_ν and L are continuous. Therefore E_ν has the structure of a Fréchet space and $j_\nu = \mathrm{pr}_{\mathscr{E}(\omega)}$ is also continuous.

By the Banach theorem, either $j_\nu(E_\nu) = \mathscr{E}(\omega)$ or $j_\nu(E_\nu)$ is a set of first category. The first possibility is ruled out by the previous remark. Thus $j_\nu(E_\nu)$ is of first category and therefore also $\bigcup_{\nu \geq 0}^{\infty} j_\nu(E_\nu)$. It follows then that one can find $f \in \mathscr{E}(\omega_0) - \bigcup_{\nu \geq 0}^{\infty} j_\nu(E_\nu)$. This answers our question.

Concluding remark. The example studied in this chapter is due to H. Lewy (see [18]). The methods we have employed help to decide whether or not the complex Q*(S) associated with the tangential Cauchy-Riemann equations presents a phenomenon similar to that considered by Lewy, i.e. the absence of the Poincaré lemma. This is what one could call the Lewy problem.

Exercise. What information gives you the Mayer-Vietoris sequence in the example we have discussed for cohomology in dimension zero?

3. Complexes of Differential Operators with Constant Coefficients

1. Stating the Problem

Let Ω be an open set in $\mathbf{R}^n$ and let $\mathscr{E}(\Omega)$ be the space of C^∞ functions on Ω, $\mathscr{D}(\Omega)$ the subspace of $\mathscr{E}(\Omega)$ of those functions with compact support in Ω. We set $\mathscr{E}^s(\Omega) = \mathscr{E}(\Omega) \times \ldots \times \mathscr{E}(\Omega)$ s-times and similarly for $\mathscr{D}^s(\Omega)$.

Given a matrix $A = (a_{ij}(\xi))_{\substack{1 \leqslant i \leqslant p \\ 1 \leqslant j \leqslant q}}$ with polynomial entries in the variables $\xi_1, \ldots \xi_n$, replacing ξ_i with the symbol $\dfrac{\partial}{\partial x_i} = D_i$ we get a differential operator A(D). We can consider A(D) as a map

$$(0) \quad \mathscr{E}^q(\Omega) \xrightarrow{A(D)} \mathscr{E}^p(\Omega).$$

One is led to consider the system of partial differential equations

$$(1) \quad A(D)u = f \quad \text{for } f \in \mathscr{E}^p(\Omega) \quad \text{and} \quad u \in \mathscr{E}^q(\Omega).$$

Remark 1. If (1) is solvable and if $Q(\xi) = (Q_1(\xi), \ldots Q_p(\xi))$ is a polynomial matrix such that

$$(2) \quad Q(D)\,A(D) = 0, \text{ then necessarily } Q(D)f = 0.$$

Remark 2. If (1) is solvable and if $Q(\xi) = \begin{pmatrix} Q_1(\xi) \\ \vdots \\ Q_q(\xi) \end{pmatrix}$ is a polynomial matrix such that

$$(3) \quad A(D)\,Q(D) \equiv 0, \text{ then for any}$$

$$v \in \mathscr{E}(\Omega),\ u + Q(D)\,v \text{ is also a solution of (1).}$$

Obviously the solutions $Q(\xi)$ of (2) form a module over the ring $\mathscr{P}$ of polynomials and thus we can find a finite basis. This will give an operator B(D) such that

$$(4)\quad \mathscr{E}^q(\Omega) \xrightarrow{A(D)} \mathscr{E}^p(\Omega) \xrightarrow{B(D)} \mathscr{E}^r(\Omega)$$

is a complex "as exact as possible."

Similarly for the solution $Q(\xi)$ of (3) which will give another operator C(D) such that

$$(5)\quad \mathscr{E}^s(\Omega) \xrightarrow{C(D)} \mathscr{E}^q(\Omega) \xrightarrow{A(D)} \mathscr{E}^p(\Omega) \xrightarrow{B(D)} \mathscr{E}^r(\Omega)$$

is a complex "as exact as possible."

We thus have to consider the *problem of inserting a differential operator A(D) into a complex of differential operators having a Poincaré lemma.*

2. Hilbert Theorem (Forward Resolution)

a) A satisfactory answer to the problem stated above is provided by some theorems of Ehrenpreis, Løjasiewicz (for an essential step) and Malgrange (for the most general form of the statements). We limit ourselves to stating basic theorems of this theory.

Theorem A: Let Ω be an open convex set in $\mathbf{R}^n$. The necessary and sufficient condition for the system (1) to have a solution $u \in \mathscr{E}^q(\Omega)$ for a given $f \in \mathscr{E}^p(\Omega)$ is that: for any polynomial vector $Q(\xi)$ such that $Q(\xi)\, A(\xi) \equiv 0$ we should have also $Q(D)f = 0$.

From this one easily deduces the following.

Corollary: The necessary and sufficient condition for a sequence of differential operators

$$\mathscr{E}^p(\Omega) \xrightarrow{A(D)} \mathscr{E}^q(\Omega) \xrightarrow{B(D)} \mathscr{E}^r(\Omega)$$

to be exact on any open convex set $\Omega \subset \mathbf{R}^n$ is that the sequence of $\mathscr{P}$-homomorphisms

$$\mathscr{P}^r \xrightarrow{{}^tB(\xi)} \mathscr{P}^q \xrightarrow{{}^tA(\xi)} \mathscr{P}^p$$

be an exact sequence $(\mathscr{P} = \mathbf{C}[\xi_1, \ldots, \xi_n])$.

The sufficiency of the condition is a direct consequence of Theorem A. The necessity should have additional argument. However, we will omit it as only the sufficiency part is of practial interest.

b) By virtue of the above corollary the problem to continue the differential operator A(D) to the right with a complex of differential operators with constant coefficients is reduced to a purely algebraic problem, and the solution is provided by a classical theorem of Hilbert that we state in the following form.

Hilbert's theorem: Let $\mathcal{P} = \mathbf{C}[\xi_1, \ldots, \xi_n]$. *Given a* $\mathcal{P}$*-homomorphism*

$$\mathcal{P}^{p_1} \xrightarrow{\alpha_1} \mathcal{P}^{p_0}$$

one can find an exact sequence of $\mathcal{P}$*-homomorphisms*

$$0 \longrightarrow \mathcal{P}^{p_d} \xrightarrow{\alpha_d} \mathcal{P}^{p_{d-1}} \longrightarrow \ldots \xrightarrow{\alpha_3} \mathcal{P}^{p_2} \xrightarrow{\alpha_2} \mathcal{P}^{p_1} \xrightarrow{\alpha_1} \mathcal{P}^{p_0}$$

of length $d \leqslant n$ $(d = 2$ if $n = 1)$.

Taking thus for α_1 the homomorphism given by the matrix ${}^tA(\xi) = {}^tA_0(\xi)$ (so that $p_0 = p$, $p_1 = q$) and representing the homomorphisms α_i, $i > 1$, by polynomial matrices ${}^tA_i(\xi)$, we then obtain a complex of differential operators

$$\mathscr{E}^{p_0}(\Omega) \xrightarrow{A_0(D)} \mathscr{E}^{p_1}(\Omega) \xrightarrow{A_1(D)} \mathscr{E}^{p_2}(\Omega) \longrightarrow \ldots \xrightarrow{A_d(D)} \mathscr{E}^{p_d}(\Omega) \longrightarrow 0$$

which is exact whenever Ω is open and convex.

c) One may ask what the situation will be if we replace the space $\mathscr{E}(\Omega)$ with the space $\mathscr{D}(\Omega)$ of functions with compact support. Again from the theory of division of distributions one can derive the following.

Proposition. Let Ω *be open and convex in* $\mathbf{R}^n$. *The necessary and sufficient condition for the sequence of differential operators*

$$\mathscr{D}^q(\Omega) \xrightarrow{A(D)} \mathscr{D}^p(\Omega) \xrightarrow{B(D)} \mathscr{D}^r(\Omega)$$

to be exact is that the sequence of $\mathcal{P}$*-homomorphisms*

$$\mathcal{P}^q \xrightarrow{A(\xi)} \mathcal{P}^p \xrightarrow{B(\xi)} \mathcal{P}^r$$

be an exact sequence.

In particular from the Hilbert resolution for which we have α_i represented by a matrix $B_i(\xi)$, one derives the complex

$$0 \longrightarrow \mathscr{D}^{p_d}(\Omega) \xrightarrow{B_d(D)} \mathscr{D}^{p_{d-1}}(\Omega) \xrightarrow{B_{d-1}(D)} \ldots \xrightarrow{B_2(D)} \mathscr{D}^{p_1}(\Omega) \xrightarrow{B_1(D)} \mathscr{D}^{p_0}(\Omega)$$

which is exact on convex open sets.

This situation is actually the "dual" situation of the one treated above as $B_i(D) = {}^tA_i(D)$.

3. Backward Resolutions

Let us consider the operator $A(D)$ and the corresponding Hilbert resolution

$$0 \longrightarrow \mathcal{P}^{p_d} \xrightarrow{\alpha_d} \mathcal{P}^{p_{d-1}} \longrightarrow \ldots \longrightarrow \mathcal{P}^{p_1} \xrightarrow{\alpha_1} \mathcal{P}^{p_0} \longrightarrow N \longrightarrow 0$$

where $\alpha_1 = {}^tA_1(\xi)$, $p_1 = p$, $p_0 = q$, and where $N = \operatorname{Coker} \alpha_1$.

If it is at all possible to extend the corresponding complex of differential operators on the left (keeping the Poincaré lemma on convex sets)

$$\cdots \longrightarrow \mathscr{E}^{p_{-1}}(\Omega) \longrightarrow \mathscr{E}^{p_0}(\Omega) \xrightarrow{A(D)} \mathscr{E}^{p_1}(\Omega) \longrightarrow \cdots \longrightarrow \mathscr{E}^{p_d}(\Omega) \longrightarrow 0,$$

we realize that it is necessary and sufficient that N be imbeddable in a finitely generated free module $\mathscr{P}^{p_{-1}}$. This is equivalent to saying that N is free of torsion:

$$\tau(N) = 0$$

where $\tau(N)$ denotes the torsion module of N.

If $\tau(N) = 0$ then we do have several ways of imbedding N into a free $\mathscr{P}$-module. The best (for reasons that will be left obscure) is to consider $N^* = \mathrm{Hom}(N, \mathscr{P})$, and to take a basis $\alpha_1 \ldots \alpha_l$ of N^* and consider the imbedding

$$N \longrightarrow \mathscr{P}^l$$

given by

$$n \longrightarrow (\alpha_1(n), \ldots, \alpha_l(n))$$

(*stable* imbedding).

We can then repeat the argument for $\mathscr{P}^l/N = N_1$ and so forth. One arrives at the following

Theorem: *The necessary and sufficient condition that the finitely generated $\mathscr{P}$-module N be included in an exact sequence of length k*

$$0 \longrightarrow N \xrightarrow{\beta_0} \mathscr{P}^{p_{-1}} \xrightarrow{\beta_1} \mathscr{P}^{p_{-2}} \xrightarrow{\beta_2} \mathscr{P}^{p_{-3}} \longrightarrow \cdots \longrightarrow \mathscr{P}^{p_{-k}}$$

of stable maps is that

i) *for* $k = 1$, $\tau(N) = 0$

ii) *for* $k = 2$, $\tau(N) = 0$ *and* $N = N^{**}$ (i.e. N be reflexive)

iii) *for* $k > 2$, $N = N^{**}$ *and* $\mathrm{Ext}^j(N^*, \mathscr{P}) = 0$ *for* $1 \leqslant j \leqslant k-2$.

This theorem can be found in a slightly different form in Palamodov [24]. Therefore the theorems of Hilbert and Palamodov provide all the necessary information to include A(D) in the longest possible complex of differential operators with constant coefficients keeping the Poincaré lemma.

Example: Let $n = 4$, $\mathscr{P} = \mathbf{C}[x, y, z, t]$. One has the maximal Hilbert resolution

$$0 \longrightarrow \mathscr{P} \xrightarrow{\alpha_3} \mathscr{P}^4 \xrightarrow{\alpha_2} \mathscr{P}^4 \xrightarrow{\alpha_1} \mathscr{P} \longrightarrow N \longrightarrow 0$$

where α_i is given by the matrix

$$\alpha_1 = (xz, xt, yz, yt), \quad \alpha_2 = \begin{pmatrix} t & y & 0 & 0 \\ -z & 0 & 0 & y \\ 0 & -x & t & 0 \\ 0 & 0 & -z & -x \end{pmatrix}, \quad \alpha_3 = \begin{pmatrix} y \\ -t \\ -x \\ z \end{pmatrix}$$

and where $N = \text{Coker}\ \alpha_1$ is such that $\tau(N) = N$.

Correspondingly one has the complex of differential operators

$$(1) \quad \mathscr{E}(\Omega) \xrightarrow{A_1} \mathscr{E}^4(\Omega) \xrightarrow{A_2} \mathscr{E}^4(\Omega) \xrightarrow{A_3} \mathscr{E}(\Omega) \longrightarrow 0$$

where

$$A_1(D) = \begin{pmatrix} \dfrac{\partial^2}{\partial x \partial z} \\ \dfrac{\partial^2}{\partial x \partial t} \\ \dfrac{\partial^2}{\partial y \partial z} \\ \dfrac{\partial^2}{\partial y \partial t} \end{pmatrix}, \quad A_2(D) = \begin{pmatrix} \partial/\partial t & -\partial/\partial z & 0 & 0 \\ \partial/\partial y & 0 & -\partial/\partial x & 0 \\ 0 & 0 & \partial/\partial t & -\partial/\partial z \\ 0 & \partial/\partial y & 0 & -\partial/\partial x \end{pmatrix},$$

$A_3(D) = (\partial/\partial y, -\partial/\partial t, -\partial/\partial x, \partial/\partial z)$.

Complex (1) is exact on open convex sets. Note that the kernel of $A_1(D)$ is the set of functions $g : \Omega \longrightarrow \mathbf{C}$ of the form

$$g = a(x, y) + b(z, t)$$

with a, b, C^∞ in their respective variables.

4. Generic Koszul Complex

a) It has been said that "in natural phenomena one does not ask what happens in all cases but what happens in the majority of cases."[(1)] Accepting this point of view one can be satisfied to have an explicit resolution of a generic polynomial homomorphism

$$\mathscr{P}^s \xrightarrow{A(\xi)} \mathscr{P}^r$$

represented by a matrix $A(\xi) = (a_{ij}(\xi))_{\substack{1 \leqslant i \leqslant r \\ 1 \leqslant j \leqslant s}}$.

1. "In naturalibus non quaeritur quid semper fiat sed quid in pluribus accidat." Thomas Aquinas, *Summa Theologica*.

As the matrix is generic, it will have maximal rank (over the field of rational functions in the variables ξ). We will first assume $r \leqslant s$.

We want to make precise the notion for $A(\xi)$ to be generic and to state for generic A the corresponding Hilbert resolution.

b) Let $\mathcal{M}_{r \times s}(\mathbf{C}) = \mathrm{Hom}_C(\mathbf{C}^s, \mathbf{C}^r)$ be the space of matrices of type $r \times s$ with entries in $\mathbf{C}$. The group $GL(r, \mathbf{C}) \times GL(s, \mathbf{C})$ operates on $\mathcal{M}_{r \times s}(\mathbf{C})$ by

$$(\alpha, \beta, M) \longrightarrow \alpha M \beta (\alpha \in GL(r, \mathbf{C}), M \in \mathcal{M}_{r \times s}(\mathbf{C}), \beta \in GL(s, \mathbf{C})).$$

The space $\mathcal{M}_{r \times s}(\mathbf{C})$ gets partitioned into orbits according to the action of this group, one for each value of the rank of M. Denoting by J_ϱ the orbit where the rank equals $r - \varrho$ (i.e. drops by ϱ units) we thus have

$$\mathcal{M}_{r \times s}(\mathbf{C}) = J_0 \cup J_1 \cup \ldots \cup J_r.$$

One easily verifies that

$$\bar{J}_\varrho = J_\varrho \cup J_{\varrho+1} \cup \ldots \cup J_r$$

is an algebraic irreducible variety of codimension $\varrho(s - r + \varrho)$. Given a matrix $A(\xi)$ of type $r \times s$ with polynomial entries one can consider the map

$$\alpha : \mathbf{C}^n \longrightarrow \mathcal{M}_{r \times s}(\mathbf{C})$$

given by $\xi \longrightarrow A(\xi)$. One can then consider the algebraic variety

$$V_A = \alpha^{-1}(\bar{J}_1)$$

of points in $\mathbf{C}^n$ where the rank of A drops at least by one. Since $\bar{J}_1$ is irreducible, one then verifies without great difficulty that *either* $V_A = \phi$ *or else each irreducible component of* V_A *has a dimension* $\geqslant n - (s - r + 1)$.

Given the matrix $A = (a_{ij}(\xi))$ one can consider all submatrices $A' = (a_{ij}(\xi))_{\substack{1 \leqslant i \leqslant r' \\ 1 \leqslant j < s'}}$ with $r' \leqslant s'$ and the corresponding algebraic varieties $V_{A'}$. We say that *A is generic* if for each choice of A', $V_{A'}$ is either empty or of mimimal dimension $(n - (s' - r' + 1))$. For instance, if the map α associated to A is transversal to the stratification just described of $\mathcal{M}_{r \times s}(\mathbf{C})$ (after a suitable rearrangement of row and column of A), then A is a generic matrix.

c) Let $A = (a_{ij}(\xi))$ be a generic matric of type $r \times s$, $r \leqslant s$.

Let us introduce the following spaces.

$\mathcal{A}^\ell$ = space of exterior forms in the indeterminates $dt_1, \ldots, dt_s$, of degree ℓ and with polynomial coefficients.

Thus an element $\omega \in \mathcal{A}^\ell$ has an expression

$$\omega = \Sigma_{1 \leqslant i_1 < \ldots < i_\ell \leqslant s} \, \omega_{i_1 \ldots i_\ell}(\xi) \, dt_{i_1} \wedge \ldots \wedge dt_{i_\ell} \quad (\omega_{i_1 \ldots i_\ell}(\xi) \in \mathcal{P}).$$

$\mathscr{B}^h_k$ = space of homogeneous polynomials of degree k in the indeterminates $y_1, \ldots, y_r$ and with coefficients in $\mathscr{A}^h$.

Thus an element $\beta \in \mathscr{B}^h_k$ has an expression

$$\beta = \sum_{|\alpha| = k} \beta_{\alpha_1 \ldots \alpha_r} y_1^{\alpha_1} \ldots y_r^{\alpha_r} \quad (\beta_{\alpha_1 \ldots \alpha_r} \in \mathscr{A}^h).$$

To each row of the matrix A we associate the exterior 1-form

$$\varphi_1 = a_{11}\, dt_1 + \ldots + a_{1s}\, dt_s$$
$$\ldots\ldots\ldots\ldots\ldots\ldots\ldots\ldots$$
$$\varphi_r = a_{r1}\, dt_1 + \ldots + a_{rs}\, dt_s.$$

By exterior multiplication with φ_i we get a morphism

$$\mathscr{A}^\ell \xrightarrow{\wedge \varphi_i} \mathscr{A}^{\ell+1}.$$

Finally, if we introduce

$$\nabla = \sum_1^r \varphi_i \frac{\partial}{\partial y_i},^{(2)}$$

We define a map

$$\mathscr{B}^h_k \xrightarrow{\nabla} \mathscr{B}^{h+1}_{k-1}.$$

We can identify the map $\mathscr{P}^s \xrightarrow{A} \mathscr{P}^r$ with the map

$$\mathscr{A}^{s-1} \xrightarrow{\wedge\varphi_1 \,\vdots\, \wedge\varphi_r} (\mathscr{A}^s)^r$$

as one obviously has $\mathscr{A}^{s-1} \simeq \mathscr{P}^s$, $\mathscr{A}^s \simeq \mathscr{P}$.

Denoting by N_A the co-kernel of A we have $\tau(N_A) = N_A$ as A has generically maximal rank.

The generic Koszul complex is the following exact sequence of $\mathscr{P}$-homomorphism

$$0 \longrightarrow \mathscr{B}^0_{s-r-1} \xrightarrow{\nabla} \ldots \xrightarrow{\nabla} \mathscr{B}^{s-r-2}_1 \longrightarrow \mathscr{A}^{s-r-1} \xrightarrow{\wedge\varphi_1 \wedge \cdots \wedge \varphi_r}$$
$$\mathscr{A}^{s-1} \xrightarrow{\wedge\varphi_1 \,\vdots\, \wedge\varphi_r} (\mathscr{A}^s)^r \longrightarrow N_A \longrightarrow 0.$$

The proof of the exactness of the sequence is based on a classical theorem of Macaulay [19].

d) For example, if r = 1, i.e. A is generic with only one row, the Koszul complex reduces to the classical Koszul complex;

$$0 \longrightarrow \mathscr{A}^0 \xrightarrow{\wedge\varphi} \mathscr{A}^1 \xrightarrow{\wedge\varphi} \ldots \xrightarrow{\wedge\varphi} \mathscr{A}^{s-1} \xrightarrow{\wedge\varphi} \mathscr{A}^s \longrightarrow N \longrightarrow 0$$

2. A slight modification of the definition of ∇ is required over a field of characteristic $\neq 0$.

where $\varphi = a_1\, dt_1 + \dots a_s dt_s$.

For instance, if we takes s = n and

$$(a_1 \dots a_n) \equiv (\xi_1, \dots \xi_n),$$

we get the Koszul complex which leads to the de Rham complex of differential exterior forms in $\mathbf{R}^n$ with exterior differentiation d as operators.

If we have n = 2 m and we take s = m and

$$(a_1, \dots, a_m) = (\tfrac{1}{2}(\xi_1 + i\, \xi_{m+1}), \dots, \tfrac{1}{2}(\xi_m + i\, \xi_{2m})),$$

we obtain another Koszul complex which on $\mathbf{C}^m = \mathbf{R}^{2m}$ (with the identification $z_\alpha = x_\alpha + i\, x_{n+\alpha}$) gives the Dolbeault complex of differential exterior form of type (0, ∗) with exterior differentiation $\bar{\partial}$ as operator.

In this way we get several complexes of differential operators with constant coefficients which do cover the classical cases of de Rham and Dolbeault complexes.

NOTE: The example given at the end of the previous section is not a generalized Koszul complex.

e) Replacing the generic matrix A with its transpose, one can consider the corresponding $\mathscr{P}$-homomorphism

$$\mathscr{P}^r \xrightarrow{{}^tA} \mathscr{P}^s$$

that one could also write as

$$(\mathscr{A}^0)^r \xrightarrow{\alpha} \mathscr{A}^1$$

given by $(u_1, \dots, u_r) \longrightarrow \Sigma u_i \varphi_i$.

With similar argument *one then obtains the following exact sequence setting* $D = \Sigma\, y_i\, \varphi_i$,

$$0 \longrightarrow (\mathscr{A}^0)^r \xrightarrow{\alpha} \mathscr{A}^1 \xrightarrow{\varphi_1 \wedge \dots \wedge \varphi_r} \mathscr{A}^{r+1} \xrightarrow{D} \mathscr{B}_1^{r+2} \xrightarrow{D} \dots \xrightarrow{D}$$
$$\mathscr{B}_{s-r-2}^{s-1} \xrightarrow{D} \mathscr{B}_{s-r-1}^{s} \longrightarrow N \longrightarrow 0$$

where N is the co-kernel of the last map D.

This could be called the generic co-Koszul complex, as this was obtained from the previous one by application of the function $\mathrm{Hom}_{\mathscr{P}}(\cdot, \mathscr{P})$.

4. Boundary Value Problems for General Complexes of Differential Operators

1. Preliminaries

Our purpose is now to extend to general complexes of differential operators (with constant or variable coefficients) the considerations developed in chapter 2 about the system of Cauchy-Riemann equations. Again we restrict our attention to $\mathbf{R}^n$, although all considerations can be carried over to any differentiable manifold.

Let U be an open set in $\mathbf{R}^n$ and $\varrho : U \longrightarrow \mathbf{R}$ be a C^∞ function; we set as usual.

$$U^+ = \{x \in U | \varrho(x) \geqslant 0\}, U^- = \{x \in U | \varrho(x) \leqslant 0\},$$
$$S = \{x \in U | \varrho(x) = 0\}$$

and assume $d\varrho \neq 0$ on S.

Let E^j be a sequence of differentiable vector bundles over U. In general $E^j = U \times \mathbf{C}^{p_j}$ will be the trivial bundle of rank p_j. We set

$$\mathscr{E}^j(U) = \Gamma(U, E^j) = \text{space of } C^\infty \text{ sections of } E^j \text{ over } U.$$

We assume that we do have a complex of spaces $\mathscr{E}^j(U)$ and partial differntial operators.

$$\mathscr{E}^*(U) \equiv \{\mathscr{E}^0(U) \xrightarrow{D^0} \mathscr{E}^1(U) \xrightarrow{D^1} \mathscr{E}^2(U) \xrightarrow{D^2} \dots \}.$$

Each D^j, locally, is expressed by a matrix of partial differential operators

$$D^j \equiv (\Sigma\, a_\alpha(x)_{hk} D^\alpha)_{\substack{1 \leqslant h \leqslant r_j \\ 1 \leqslant k \leqslant s_j}}$$

with coefficients $a_\alpha(x)_{hk}$ C^∞ on U.

By assumption we have

$$D^{j+1} D^j = 0.$$

If $\mathscr{F}^j(U, U^\pm) \equiv \{s \in \mathscr{E}^j(U) | s \equiv 0 \text{ on } U^\pm\}$, we can define $\mathscr{E}^j(U^\pm) = \mathscr{E}^j(U)/\mathscr{F}^j(U, U^\pm)$ and we obtain in this way two other complexes $\mathscr{E}^*(U^\pm)$.

Examples.

1) One has the classical de Rham and Dolbeault complexes. More generally one has all complexes that come from a Koszul complex. For instance, if $(\varphi_1(\xi), \ldots, \varphi_s(\xi))$ are polynomials in n variables $\xi = (\xi_1 \ldots \xi_n)$ and if the variety of common complex zeros to $(\varphi_1(\xi), \ldots, \varphi_l(\xi))$ is either empty or of dimension n–l (l = 1, 2, ..., s), then one can consider the spaces $\mathscr{E}^{(j)}(U)$ of exterior differential forms of degree j in the indeterminates $dt_1, \ldots, dt_s$ and the complex

$$\mathscr{E}^{(0)}(U) \xrightarrow{\partial_\varphi} \mathscr{E}^{(1)}(U) \xrightarrow{\partial_\varphi} \mathscr{E}^{(2)}(U) \xrightarrow{\partial_\varphi} \ldots \xrightarrow{\partial_\varphi} \mathscr{E}^{(s)}(U) \longrightarrow 0$$

where, for $\omega = \Sigma_{i_1 < \ldots < i_l} \omega_{i_1 \ldots i_l}(x)\, dt_{i_1} \wedge \ldots \wedge dt_{i_l}$, we have set

$$\partial_\varphi \omega = \sum_{i_0 < \ldots < i_l} (\Sigma(-1)^h \varphi_{i_h}(D)\, \omega_{i_0 \ldots \hat{i_h} \ldots i_l}(x))\, dt_{i_0} \wedge \ldots \wedge dt_{i_l}.$$

2) As an example of a complex of differential operators with variable coefficients, one can take the complex of $\bar{\partial}_S$ considered in chapter 2.

2. Cauchy Data

We now introduce the hypersurface S into the picture.

For $u \in \mathscr{E}^j(U)$ we set

$$u^0 = \begin{cases} u \text{ on } U^+ \\ 0 \text{ on } \overset{0}{U}{}^- \end{cases}$$

and consider u^0 as a distribution on U. We then define

$$\mathscr{I}^j(U, S) = \{u \in \mathscr{E}^j(U) \,|\, D^j u^0 = (D^j u)^0\}.$$

In other words, if

$${}^t\mathscr{E}^j(U) = \Gamma\,(U, {}^*E^j \oplus \wedge^n T^*)$$

denote the space of section of the "dual" bundle (actually the dual bundle tensored with the canonical bundle) and if

$${}^tD^j : {}^t\mathscr{E}^j(U) \longleftarrow {}^t\mathscr{E}^{j+1}(U)$$

is the formal transpose of the operator D^j, then

$$u \in \mathscr{I}^j(U, S) \Leftrightarrow \int_{U^+} < \varphi, D^j u > \; = \int_{U^+} < {}^tD^j\varphi, u > \;\forall\, \varphi \in {}^t\mathscr{E}^j(U)$$

with compact support in U. We obtain in this way a subcomplex of $\mathscr{E}^*(U)$

$$\mathscr{I}^*(U, S) = \{\mathscr{I}^0(U, S) \xrightarrow{D^0} \mathscr{I}^1(U, S) \xrightarrow{D^1} \mathscr{I}^2(U, S) \xrightarrow{D^2} \ldots\}.$$

Indeed if $u \in \mathcal{I}^j(U, S)$, $D^{j+1}(D^j u)^0 = D^{j+1} D^j(u^0) \equiv 0$ as $D^{j+1} D^j = 0$. But also $(D^{j+1} D^j u)^0 = 0$. Thus $D^{j+1}(D^j u)^0 = (D^{j+1} D^j u)^0)$.

Therefore we can consider the quotient complex

$$Q^*(S) = \{Q^0(S) \xrightarrow{D^0_S} Q^1(S) \xrightarrow{D^1_S} Q^2(S) \xrightarrow{D^2_S} \ldots\}$$

defined by the exact sequence

$$0 \longrightarrow \mathcal{I}^*(U, S) \longrightarrow C^*(U) \longrightarrow Q^*(S) \longrightarrow 0.$$

We note that the space $\mathcal{I}^j(U, S)$ is the space of $u \in \mathcal{E}^j(U)$ with *zero Cauchy data on S* with respect to the operator D^j. Thus the space $Q^j(S)$, which is obviously concentrated on S, is the space of *Cauchy data* on S for the operator D_j. Also the operators D^j_S having local character are certainly differential operators by Peetre's theorem as soon as the spaces $Q^l(S)$ are free $\mathcal{E}(S)$ modules.

Examples.

1) For the de Rham complex we have

$$\mathcal{I}^j(U, S) = \{\varphi^j \in \mathcal{E}^{(j)}(U) \mid \varphi^j = \varrho\alpha^j + d\varrho \wedge \beta^{j-1}\}, d_S = d.$$

2) For the Dolbeault complex

$$\mathcal{I}^j(U, S) = \{\varphi^j \in \mathcal{E}^{(o\ j)}(U) \mid \varphi^j = \varrho\alpha^j + \bar{\partial}\varrho \wedge \beta^{j-1}\}$$

and $\bar{\partial}_S$ gives the tangential Cauchy-Riemann complex.

3) For the complex

$$\mathcal{E}(U) \xrightarrow{\Delta} \mathcal{E}(U) \longrightarrow 0$$

where $\Delta = \Sigma \dfrac{\partial^2}{\partial x_i^2}$, we get

$$\mathcal{I}^0(U, S) = \varrho^2 \mathcal{E}(U), \mathcal{I}^1(U, S) = \mathcal{E}(U)$$

so that the tangential complex reduces to

$$\mathcal{E}^2(S) \longrightarrow 0.$$

3. Noncharacteristic Hypersurfaces

Let

$$\mathcal{F}^j(U, S) = \{u \in \mathcal{E}^j(U) \mid u \text{ is flat on } S\}.$$

Clearly

$$\mathscr{F}^*(U, S) = \{\mathscr{F}^0(U, S) \xrightarrow{D^0} \mathscr{F}^1(U, S) \xrightarrow{D^1} \mathscr{F}^2(U, S) \xrightarrow{D^2} \dots\}$$

is a subcomplex of $\mathscr{I}^*(U, S)$(and thus of $\mathscr{E}^*(U)$): $\mathscr{F}^*(U, S) \subset \mathscr{I}^*(U, S) \subset C^*(U)$.

In particular we can consider the quotient complex

$$\frac{\mathscr{I}^*(U, S)}{\mathscr{F}^*(U, S)} = \{\mathscr{I}^0(S)[\varrho] \xrightarrow{D^0} \mathscr{I}^1(S)[\varrho] \xrightarrow{D^1} \mathscr{I}^2(S)[\varrho] \xrightarrow{D^2} \dots\}.$$

By Whitney's extension theorem (actually from the simple fact that on a hypersurface one can prescribe arbitrarily the normal derivatives of a "trace" of a C^∞ function) one has that $\mathscr{I}^j(S)[\varrho] = \dfrac{\mathscr{I}^j(U, S)}{\mathscr{F}^j(U, S)}$ = space of formal power series expansions in ϱ of the elements of $\mathscr{I}^j(U, S)$.

Definition. We say that the hypersurface S is *noncharacteristic* (formally) if the complex $\mathscr{I}^*(U, S)/\mathscr{F}^*(U, S)$ is acyclic in any dimension, i.e. if we have an exact sequence

$$0 \longrightarrow \mathscr{I}^0(S)[\varrho] \xrightarrow{D^0} \mathscr{I}^1(S)[\varrho] \xrightarrow{D^1} \mathscr{I}^2(S)[\varrho] \xrightarrow{D^2} \dots.$$

Examples. 1) For the de Rham, Dolbeault complex or for the complex of the Laplace equation every hypersurface S is noncharacteristic. The proof has already been given for the Dolbeault complex. The same proof holds for the de Rham complex. For the Laplace operator it is a straightforward verification.

2) In $\mathbf{R}^{n+1}$, where $t, x_1, \dots, x_n$ are the coordinates, consider the operator $D = \dfrac{\partial^2}{\partial t^2} - \Sigma\, a_{ij} \dfrac{\partial^2}{\partial x_i\, \partial x_j}$ and let

$$\sigma_D(\eta, \xi_1 \dots \xi_n) = \eta^2 - \Sigma\, a_{ij}\, \xi_i\, \xi_j.$$

For the complex

$$\mathscr{E}(U) \xrightarrow{D} \mathscr{E}(U) \longrightarrow 0$$

a surface $S = \{\varrho = 0\}$ is noncharacteristic if σ_D (grad ϱ) $\neq 0$ at each point of S. In this case $\mathscr{I}^0(U, S) = \varrho^2 \mathscr{E}(U)$ and $\mathscr{I}^1(U, S) = \mathscr{E}(U)$. So the tangential complex reduces to

$$\mathscr{E}^2(S) \longrightarrow 0.$$

4. Mayer-Vietoris Sequence

We set

$$\begin{aligned} H^*(U) &= H^*(C^*(U)) \\ H^*(U^{\pm}) &= H^*(C^*(U^{\pm})) \\ H^*(S) &= H^*(Q^*(S)). \end{aligned}$$

Theorem: If S is noncharacteristic, then we have an exact sequence

$$\begin{aligned} 0 \longrightarrow H^0(U) &\longrightarrow H^0(U^+) \oplus H^0(U^-) \longrightarrow H^0(S) \longrightarrow \\ \longrightarrow H^1(U) &\longrightarrow H^1(U^+) \oplus H^1(U^-) \longrightarrow H^1(S) \longrightarrow \dots . \end{aligned}$$

The proof is the same as the one given in the second chapter.

Remark. We can replace the spaces $\mathscr{E}^j(U)$ with the spaces $\mathscr{D}^j(U) = \{u \in \mathscr{E}^j(\Omega) | \text{supp } u \text{ compact in } U\}$, and similarly for $\mathscr{E}^j(U^{\pm})$, $\mathscr{I}^j(U, S)$, etc.

We can then define the notion of noncharacteristic with respect to compact supports. If S is noncharacteristic with respect to compact supports, then one has a Mayer-Vietoris sequence in which each cohomology group is replaced with the corresponding group with compact support.

In particular *if S is non-characteristic and compact, no further assumption is needed to write the Mayer-Vietoris sequence with compact supports.*

5. Applications

a) *Removable singularities.* Let $A_0(\xi)$, $A_1(\xi)$ be two matrices with polynomial entries of type $p_1 \times p_0$ and $p_2 \times p_1$ such that

$$A_1(\xi)A_0(\xi) = 0.$$

Let us consider the complex of differential operators

$$\mathscr{E}^{p_0}(\mathbf{R}^n) \xrightarrow{A_0(D)} \mathscr{E}^{p_1}(\mathbf{R}^n) \xrightarrow{A_1(D)} \mathscr{E}^{p_2}(\mathbf{R}).$$

We will make the following assumptions:

1) $A_0(D)$ is an elliptic operator, i.e. any $u \in \mathscr{E}^{p_0}(\Omega)$ (Ω open in $\mathbf{R}^n$) such that $A(D)u = 0$ is real analytic (complex valued).

2) The sequence of $\mathscr{P}$-homomorphisms

$$\mathscr{P}^{p_0} \xrightarrow{A_0(\xi)} \mathscr{P}^{p_1} \xrightarrow{A_1(\xi)} \mathscr{P}^{p_2}$$

is an exact sequence.

3) We can find a compact hypersurface $S \subset \mathbf{R}^3$ such that

(α) S is noncharacteristic,

(β) $\mathbf{R}^n - S$ consists of two connected components.

Then we must also have

$$H^0(U^-) \simeq H^0(S)$$

where U^- is the closure of the bounded component of $\mathbf{R}^n - S$. In other words, any solution f on S of the tangential operator $(A_0)_S f = 0$ is the restriction to S of a unique solution u in U^- of the equations $A_0 u = 0$ which is C^∞ up to S; $r_S u = f$.

Proof. As S is compact and noncharacteristic, we can write the Mayer-Vietoris sequence with compact supports for $U = \mathbf{R}^n$:

$$0 \longrightarrow H^0_k(\mathbf{R}^n) \longrightarrow H^0_k(U^+) \oplus H^0(U^-) \longrightarrow H^0(S) \longrightarrow$$
$$\longrightarrow H^1_k(\mathbf{R}^n) \longrightarrow \dots .$$

By the first assumption we must have $H^0_k(\mathbf{R}^n) = 0 = H^0_k(U^+)$. By the second assumption and the second proposition of the previous chapter (applied to $\Omega = \mathbf{R}^n$), we derive $H^1_k(\mathbf{R}^n) = 0$. It follows that

$$H^0(U^-) \longrightarrow H^0(S)$$

is an isomorphism.

Examples. (α) To be able to construct some general example that will fit into this situation we need to mention a local criterion to recognize when a hypersurface is noncharacteristic. We will give the criterion for operators with constant coefficients. The general case is similar except that one has to assume the constancy of the order of the differential operator in the region where one considers it.

Let

$$\mathscr{E}^j(U) \xrightarrow{D^j} \mathscr{E}^{j+1}(U)$$

be a partial differential operator defined in some open set $U \subset \mathbf{R}^n$ and with constant coefficients:

$$D^j = \Sigma_{|\alpha| \leqslant k} a_\alpha D^\alpha$$

and for some α with $|\alpha| = k$, $a_\alpha \neq 0$. We set

$$\sigma_\xi(D^j) = \Sigma_{|\alpha| = k} a_\alpha \xi^\alpha$$

(principal symbol of D^j) so that, at any point $x \in U$, $\sigma_\xi(D^j)$ can be considered as a linear map

$$\sigma_\xi(D^j) : E^j_x \longrightarrow E^{j+1}_x$$

depending on the choice of the vector $\xi \in \mathbf{R}^n$.

Given a complex of differential operators on U, with constant coefficients

$$(*) \quad \mathscr{E}^0(U) \xrightarrow{D^0} \mathscr{E}^1(U) \xrightarrow{D^1} \mathscr{E}^2(U) \xrightarrow{D^2} \dots$$

for any vector $\xi \in \mathbf{R}^n$ and any point $x_0 \in U$ one can consider the "symbol sequence"

$$0 \longrightarrow E^0_{x_0} \xrightarrow{\sigma_\xi(D^0)} E^1_{x_0} \xrightarrow{\sigma_\xi(D^1)} E^2_{x_0} \xrightarrow{\sigma_\xi(D^2)} \cdots .$$

We say that the direction $\xi \in \mathbf{R}^n - \{0\}$ at x_0 is noncharacteristic if the symbol sequence is exact.

A hypersurface $S = \{\varrho = 0\}$ on U is called noncharacteristic at the point $x_0 \in S$ for the complex (*) if the vector $(\text{grad } \varrho)_{x_0} = \xi$ is a noncharacteristic vector.

One has the following criterion: *If the hypersurface S is noncharacteristic at each point, then S is a noncharacteristic hypersurface* (in the sense of the definition given in section 3).

β) Let us now consider the Koszul complex associated with a sequence of polynomials $(\varphi_1(\xi), \ldots, \varphi_m(\xi))$ that we will assume homogeneous and of the same degree k.

Setting $\varphi(\xi, dt) = \overset{m}{\Sigma}\varphi_i(\xi)dt_i$ the Koszul complex is

$$(1) \quad 0 \longrightarrow \mathscr{A}^0 \xrightarrow{\wedge\varphi} \mathscr{A}^1 \xrightarrow{\wedge\varphi} \mathscr{A}^2 \xrightarrow{\wedge\varphi} \cdots$$

and to it corresponds the complex of differential operators

$$\mathscr{E}^{(0)}(\mathbf{R}^n) \xrightarrow{\partial_\varphi} \mathscr{E}^{(1)}(\mathbf{R}^n) \xrightarrow{\partial_\varphi} \mathscr{E}^{(2)}(\mathbf{R}^n) \xrightarrow{\partial_\varphi} \cdots$$

where $\mathscr{E}^{(j)}(\mathbf{R}^n)$ is the space of C^∞ exterior forms in $\mathbf{R}^n$ of degree j in the indeterminates $dt_1, \ldots, dt_m$ and where ∂_φ is defined by

$$\partial_\varphi\ \omega = \sum_{i_0 < \ldots < i_\ell} (\Sigma(-1)^h\, \varphi_{i_h}(D)\, \omega_{i_0 \ldots \hat{i}_h \ldots i_\ell}(x))\, dt_{i_0} \wedge \ldots \wedge dt_{i_\ell}$$

for $\omega = \sum_{i_1 < \ldots < i_\ell} \omega_{i_1 \ldots i_\ell}(x)\, dt_{i_1} \wedge \ldots \wedge dt_{i_\ell}$.

We make the following assumptions.

i) $\Sigma\,|\varphi_j(\xi)|^2 \geqslant C\,|\xi|^{2k}\ \forall\, \xi \in \mathbf{R}^n$.

ii) The ideal $\mathfrak{a} = \mathscr{P}(\varphi_1(\xi), \ldots, \varphi_m(\xi))$ is an ideal of principal class, i.e. $m \leqslant n$ and the variety of zeros of $(\varphi_1(\xi), \ldots, \varphi_j(\xi))$ in $\mathbf{C}^n$ is of dimension n–j.

iii) $m \geqslant 2$.

Assumption i) implies that $A_0 = \partial_\varphi$. The first operator in the sequence is elliptic. Assumption ii) implies exactness of the sequence (1) and thus with assumption iii), we realize that also condition 2) is satisfied.

Now for any $\xi_0 \in \mathbf{R}^n - \{0\}$ we have

$$\sigma_{\xi_0}(\partial_\varphi) = \wedge\, \varphi(\xi_0, dt).$$

Because of i) the vector $\varphi(\xi_0, dt) \neq 0$ and consequently the symbol sequence

$$0 \longrightarrow A^0_{x_0} \xrightarrow{\wedge \varphi(\xi_0, dt)} A^1_{x_0} \xrightarrow{\wedge \varphi(\xi_0, dt)} A^2_{x_0} \xrightarrow{\wedge \varphi(\xi_0, dt)} \cdots$$

(where $A^j_{x_0}$ denotes the space of exterior j-forms with constant coefficients) is also exact. By the criterion given above, then any hypersurface S in $\mathbf{R}^n$ is noncharacteristic and thus also condition 3) is satisfied by any closed hypersurface S with $\mathbf{R}^n - S$ consisting of only two connected components.

Note that the cases of the de Rham and Dolbeault complexes are included in this situation.

b) *Cauchy problem.* Let us consider a complex of differential operators with constant coefficients

$$\mathscr{E}^{p_0}(U) \xrightarrow{A_0(D)} \mathscr{E}^{p_1}(U) \xrightarrow{A_1(D)} \mathscr{E}^{p_2}(U) \xrightarrow{A_2(D)} \mathscr{E}^{p_3}(U)$$

for which we make the following assumptions:

(1) $A_0(D)$ is elliptic

(2) the sequence

$$\mathscr{P}^{p_2} \xrightarrow{A_0(\xi)} \mathscr{P}^{p_1} \xrightarrow{A_1(\xi)} \mathscr{P}^{p_0} \xrightarrow{A_2(\xi)} \mathscr{P}^{p_3}$$

is exact

(3) the sequence

$$\mathscr{P}^{p_2} \xrightarrow{{}^tA_1(\xi)} \mathscr{P}^{p_1} \xrightarrow{{}^tA_2(\xi)} \mathscr{P}^{p_0}$$

is also exact.

NOTE: one could replace conditions (2) and (3) by their "transposes" with a slightly longer proof.

Let $x_0 \in S$ be a point on which we make the following assumptions.

(α) x_0 is a strongly elliptic point of S, i.e. the Hessian of ϱ restricted to the real tangent hyperplane to S is positive definite.

(β) x_0 is a noncharacteristic point of S.

We claim that *we can find two neighborhoods* $\omega_1 \subset \omega_2$ *of* x_0 *such that for any* $f \in H^0(S \cup \omega_2)$ *we can find* $u \in H^0(\omega_1 \cap U^-)$ *such that*

$$r_S\, u = f \text{ on } S \cap \omega_1,$$

i.e. the "Cauchy problem" is locally solvable at x_0.

Proof. By a suitable choice of coordinates we may assume $z_0 = 0$ and $-\rho = x_n - g(x_1, \ldots, x_{n-1})$ with $g(0) = 0$, $\dfrac{\partial \rho}{\partial x_i}(0) = 0$ and

$$\Sigma \frac{\partial^2 g}{\partial x_i \partial x_j}(0)\, u_i\, u_j > 0 \text{ if } u \neq 0.$$

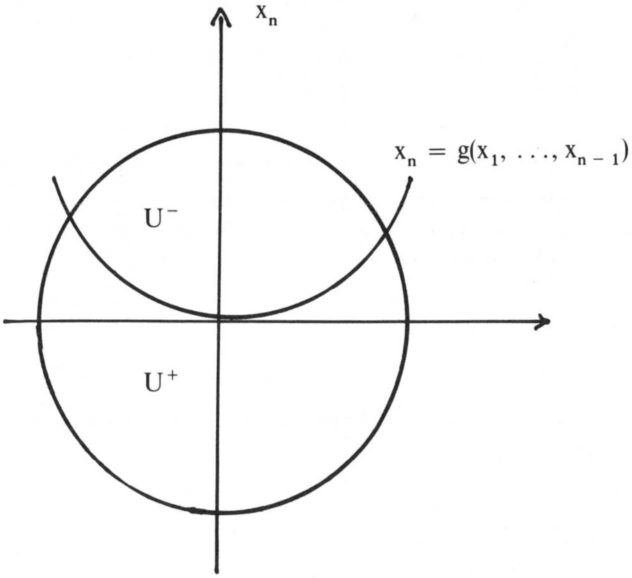

Let $0 < \varepsilon_0 < \varepsilon_1 < \varepsilon_2 < \varepsilon_3$ and $\eta > 0$ with ε_3 and η sufficiently small such that $\omega_2 = \{g(x_1, \ldots, x_{n-1}) - \eta < x_n < \varepsilon_3\} \subset\subset U$ and is convex, and set

$$\omega_1 = \{g(x_1, \ldots, x_{n-1}) - \eta < x_n < \varepsilon_0\}.$$

Because of the assumption ω_2 is a convex set and therefore by assumption (3) we have an exact sequence:

$$0 \longrightarrow H^0(\omega_2) \longrightarrow H^0(\omega_2^+) \oplus H^0(\omega_2^-) \longrightarrow H^0(S \cap \omega_2) \longrightarrow 0.$$

Thus given $f \in H^0(S \cap \omega_2)$, we can find u^+ and u^- in $H^0(\omega_2{}^{\pm})$ respectively such that

$$f = -r_S u^+ + r_S u^-.$$

Let $\tilde{u}^+$ be any C^∞ extension of u^+ to ω_2. Then

$$\operatorname{supp} A_0(D)\,\tilde{u}^+ \subset \omega_2^-.$$

Let α be a C^∞ function on ω_2 with the property $\alpha = \begin{cases} 1 \text{ for } x_n < \varepsilon_1 \\ 0 \text{ for } x_n > \varepsilon_2. \end{cases}$

Then

$$\operatorname{supp} \alpha\, A_0(D)\,\tilde{u}^+ \subset \omega_2^- \cap \{x_n \leqslant \varepsilon_2\}.$$

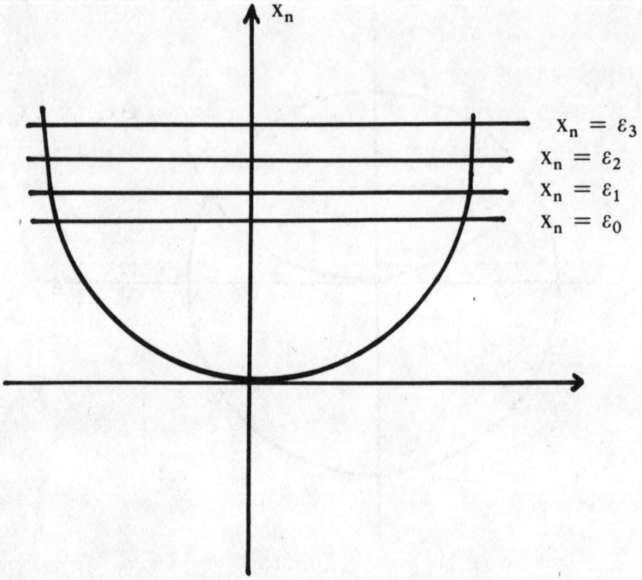

Moreover, since $A_1(D)\,A_0(D) = 0$, we must have

$$\operatorname{supp} A_1(D)\,\alpha\,A_0(D)\,\tilde{u}^+ \subset \omega_2^- \cap \{\varepsilon_1 \leqslant x_n \leqslant \varepsilon_2\} = \Lambda.$$

Let Λ_σ be a σ neighborhood of Λ such that $\Lambda_\sigma \cap \{x_n \leqslant \varepsilon_0\} = \phi$ with $0 < \sigma < \eta$. Then Λ_σ if σ is sufficiently small, is convex. Because of assumption (2) $H_k^2(\Lambda_\sigma) = 0$. Therefore we can find $h \subset \mathscr{D}^p(\Lambda_\sigma)$ such that

$$A_1(D)\,\alpha\,A_0(D)\,\tilde{u}^+ = A_1(D)\,h$$

or

$$A_1(D)(\alpha\,A_0(D)\,\tilde{u}^+ - h) = 0 \quad \text{on } \Lambda_\sigma \text{ and thus on } \omega_2.$$

Again by assumption (2), since $\alpha\,A_0(D)\,\tilde{u}^+ - h$ has compact support in ω_2, we can find $v \in \mathscr{D}^{p_0}(\omega_2)$ with

$$(*) \quad \alpha\,A_0(D)\,\tilde{u}^+ - h = A_0(D)\,v.$$

Now on $\omega_2^+ - \omega_2^+ \cap \Lambda_\sigma$ we must have $A_0(D)\,v = 0$. As v is compactly support and analytic, by assumption (1), we must have

$$\operatorname{supp} v \subset \omega_2^- \cup \Lambda_\sigma.$$

Restricting thus (*) to ω_1 we get

$$A_0(D)\,\tilde{u}^+ = A_0(D)v \quad \text{on } \omega_1$$

and supp $v \subset \omega_1^-$. Hence $\hat{u} = \tilde{u}^+ - v$ is an extension of u^+

and $$A_0(D)\,\hat{u} = 0 \quad \text{on } \omega_1.$$

Replacing
$$\begin{aligned} u^+ \text{ with } v^+ &= u^+ - \hat{u} \quad \text{on } \omega_1 \\ u^- \text{ with } v^- &= u^- - \hat{u} \quad \text{on } \omega_1 \end{aligned}$$

we get $v^+ = 0$ on ω_1^+ and thus

$$f|_{S \cap \omega_1} = r_S v^-$$

with $A_0(D)\,v^- = 0$, i.e. $v^- \in H^0(\omega^-)$.

Q.E.D.

Remarks. 1) One can show that, if $x_0 \in S$ is not an "elliptic" point, the statement may become false.

2) From the proof it follows more precisely that there exists a neighborhood ω_2 of x_0 and for every compact set $K \subset S \cap \omega_2$ a neighborhood ω_1 of x_0 with $K \subset \omega_1 \subset \omega_2$ such that for any $f \in H^0(S \cap \omega_2)$ we can find $u \in H^0(\omega_1 \cap U^-)$ with $r\,u = f$ on $S \cap \omega_1$.

5. Complexes of Differential Operators with Variable Coefficients

1. Generalities

a) Given on an open set $\Omega \subset \mathbf{R}^n$ a matrix of partial differential operators with C^∞ coefficients

$$\mathscr{E}^p(\Omega) \xrightarrow{E(x, D)} \mathscr{E}^q(\Omega),$$

one is led naturally to the following questions.

i) Find all operators Q(x, D) such that

$$Q(x, D)\, E(x, D) \equiv 0 \quad \text{(integrability conditions)}$$

ii) Find all operators S(x, D) such that

$$E(x, D)\, S(x, D) \equiv 0 \quad \text{(co-integrability conditions)}$$

Clearly if the equation

$$E(x, D)\, u(x) = f(x)$$

is solvable in u for a given f, then

i) for any integrability conditon Q(x, D) we must also have

$$Q(x, D)\, f(x) = 0; \text{ and}$$

ii) if u is a solution of the considered equation, then, for any co-integrability condition S(x, D), u + S(x, D) v is also a solution for any v.

To find all integrability and co-integrability conditions is to put the operator E inside a complex

$$\mathscr{E}^r(\Omega) \xrightarrow{S(x, D)} \mathscr{E}^p(\Omega) \xrightarrow{E(x, D)} \mathscr{E}^q(\Omega) \xrightarrow{Q(x, D)} \mathscr{E}^s(\Omega),$$

trying to choose Q and S somehow "maximal."

2. Localizing at a Point

a) Let $\Phi = \mathbf{C}\{\{x_1, \ldots, x_n\}\}$ be the ring of formal power series centered at the origin and let

$$\mathscr{D} = \Phi[D_1, \ldots, D_n],$$

be ring of partial differential operators with coefficients in Φ. Clearly $\mathscr{D}$ is not a commutative ring, because for $\alpha \in \Phi$, $[D_j, \alpha] \neq 0$ in general, for all j's.

If $a \in \mathscr{D}$, $a = \sum_{|\alpha| \leqslant k} a_\alpha(x) D^\alpha$ and for some $|\alpha| = k$, $a_\alpha \neq 0$; k is called the *order* of the operator a and $\sum_{|\alpha| = k} a_\alpha \xi^\alpha = \sigma_\xi(a)$ the *symbol* of a. If we set $\mathscr{D}_k = \{a \in \mathscr{D} | \text{ order of } a \leqslant k\}$, we get a filtration of $\mathscr{D}$

$$\mathscr{D}_0 = \Phi \subset \mathscr{D}_1 \subset \mathscr{D}_2 \subset \ldots, \cup \mathscr{D}_k = \mathscr{D},$$
$$\mathscr{D}_j \mathscr{D}_k \subset \mathscr{D}_{j+k}.$$

Therefore the associated graded ring $G\mathscr{D}$ is defined and, as

$$\sigma(a\,b) = \sigma(a)\,\sigma(b),$$

we see that $G\,\mathscr{D}$ is commutative and thus isomorphic with the graded ring $\Phi[\xi_1, \ldots \xi_n]$ of homogeneous polynomials in $\xi_1, \ldots, \xi_n$. In particular $G\mathscr{D}$ is a Noetherian ring. It follows then that *the ring $\mathscr{D}$ itself is a Noetherian ring* (as left and right module over itself).

Given a matrix $A(x, D)$ of type $p_1 \times p_0$ with entries in $\mathscr{D}$ we can associate to it a $\mathscr{D}$-homomorphism

$$\mathscr{D}^{p_1} \xrightarrow{A(x,D)} \mathscr{D}^{p_0}$$

by sending each vector $v(x, D) \in \mathscr{D}^{p_1}$, regarded as a horizontal vector $v(x, D) = (v_1(x, D), \ldots, v_{p_1}(x, D))$ into the (horizontal) vector $v(x, D)\,A(x, D)$.

In this way we see that the set of integrability conditions of $A(x, D)$ is the $\mathscr{D}$-module kernel of the $\mathscr{D}$-homomorphism A. As $\mathscr{D}^{p_1}$ is Noetherian, that $\mathscr{D}$-module is finitely generated and therefore we get an exact sequence

$$\mathscr{D}^{p_2} \xrightarrow{A_1} \mathscr{D}^{p_1} \xrightarrow{A} \mathscr{D}^{p_0}.$$

Continuing in this way one obtains a resolution going backward from the $\mathscr{D}$-module $N_A = \text{Coker } A$. It can be shown that the resolution may be chosen of length $d \leqslant n$, ($d = 2$, f $n = 1$):

$$(1)\; 0 \longrightarrow \mathscr{D}^{p_d} \xrightarrow{A_{d-1}} \mathscr{D}^{p_{d-1}} \xrightarrow{A_{d-2}} \ldots \mathscr{D}^{p_2} \xrightarrow{A_1} \mathscr{D}^{p_1} \xrightarrow{A} \mathscr{D}$$
$$\longrightarrow N_A \longrightarrow 0 (d \leqslant n) \text{(see [6])}.$$

From this we obtain a complex of differential operators on formal power series

$$(2)\quad \Phi^{p_0} \xrightarrow{A(x,D)} \Phi^{p_1} \xrightarrow{A_1(x,D)} \Phi^{p_2} \longrightarrow \cdots \longrightarrow \Phi^{p_{d-1}} \xrightarrow{A_{d-1}(x,D)} \Phi^{p_d} \longrightarrow 0.$$

Similarly the research of the co-integrability conditions leads to the problem of imbedding N_A in a finitely generated free $\mathscr{D}$-module and to choose the imbedding wisely so as to be able to extend the resolution (1) to the right as much as possible.

This will provide us with the formulations of the analogous problems solved for operators with constant coefficients by Hilbert's and Palamodov's theorems.

b) Let us assume that (1) is an exact sequence (and possibly also extended to the right as much as possible).

We can ask the following question: Is then the corresponding sequence (2) an exact sequence (i.e. is the formal Poincaré lemma true)?

In general the answer is no.

Example. In 1 variable x the complex

$$\Phi \xrightarrow{A(x,D)} \Phi \longrightarrow 0$$

where $A = x\dfrac{\partial}{\partial x}$ is not exact. However the corresponding complex of $\mathscr{D}$ modules

$$0 \longrightarrow \mathscr{D} \xrightarrow{A} \mathscr{D} \longrightarrow N_A \longrightarrow 0$$

is exact.

Remark. The complex (2) is deduced from (1) by application of the functor $\mathrm{Hom}_D(*, \Phi)$ so that:

(a) We have

$$0 \longrightarrow \mathrm{Hom}_D(N_A, \Phi) \longrightarrow \Phi^{p_0} \xrightarrow{A} \Phi^{p_1}$$

exact. This provides a description of Ker A.

(b) The complex (2) is exact if and only if

$$\mathrm{Ext}^j(N_A, \Phi) = 0 \quad \forall j > 0.$$

We realize then that given A, no matter how we may choose the resolutions, the sequence (2) may fail to be exact.

NOTE: I have learned the previous considerations from Malgrange.

c) Suppose we do have on an open set $\Omega \subset \mathbf{R}^n$ a complex of differential operators

$$(*)\quad \mathscr{E}^{p_0}(\Omega) \xrightarrow{A_0(x,D)} \mathscr{E}^{p_1}(\Omega) \xrightarrow{A_1(x,D)} \mathscr{E}^{p_2}(\Omega) \xrightarrow{A_2(x,D)} \cdots.$$

If at a point $x_0 \in \Omega$ the complex admits the Poincaré lemma, i.e. if

$$\mathscr{E}^{p_0}_{x_0} \xrightarrow{A_0} \mathscr{E}^{p_1}_{x_0} \xrightarrow{A_1} \mathscr{E}^{p_2}_{x_0} \xrightarrow{A_2} \cdots$$

is exact ($\mathscr{E}_{x_0}$ = germs of C^∞ functions at x_0), then also

$$\Phi^{p_0}_{x_0} \xrightarrow{A_0} \Phi^{p_1}_{x_0} \xrightarrow{A_1} \Phi^{p_2}_{x_0} \xrightarrow{A_2} \cdots$$

is an exact sequence (Φ_{x_0} = formal power series centered at x_0)?

Poincaré's lemma for the complex (*) at x_0 is conjectured in general to imply the formal Poincaré lemma at the same point (a thing true for constant coefficients but not clear in general), but certainly the converse is false.

Example. $n = 3$, $\mathscr{E}(\mathbf{R}^3) \xrightarrow{A} \mathscr{E}(\mathbf{R}^3) \longrightarrow 0$ where A is the Hans Lewy operator:

$$A = \frac{\partial}{\partial x_1} + i\frac{\partial}{\partial x_2} - i(x_1 + ix_2)\frac{\partial}{\partial x_3}.$$

It admits the formal Poincaré lemma at each point $x_0 \in \mathbf{R}^3$ as one verifies directly (the formal Cauchy-Kowalewsky theorem), but we have shown that the Poincaré lemma is not valid at any point $x_0 \in \mathbf{R}^3$.

3. Example of the Tangential Cauchy-Riemann Complex

a) Let N be a locally closed submanifold of $\mathbf{C}^n$ of $\dim_R N = n + l$ with $l \geqslant 0$. We are interested in the local structure of N near a point $p \in N$. We can thus assume that N is given in a neighborhood $\omega(p)$ of p in $\mathbf{C}^n$ by a set of C^∞ equations

$$\underset{1 \leqslant \alpha \leqslant n-1}{f_\alpha(z) = 0} \quad \text{with } (df_1 \wedge \ldots \wedge df_{n-1})_q \neq 0 \quad \forall\, q \in \omega \cap N.$$

A tangent vector X to $\mathbf{C}^n$ at p is an expression

$$X = \Sigma\, a_j \frac{\partial}{\partial z_j} + \Sigma\, b_j \frac{\partial}{\partial \bar{z}_j} \quad (a_j, b_j \in \mathbf{C})$$

and will be called holomorphic (anti-holomorphic) if $a_j = 0\ \forall\, j (a_j = 0\ \forall\, j)$. Let $\mathscr{I}(N) = \{f \in \mathscr{E}(\omega) | f|N = 0\}$ be the ideal of C^∞ functions vanishing on N. The vector X is tangent to N at q if

$$(X\, f)_q = 0\ \forall\, f \in \mathscr{I}(N),\ q \in N$$

i.e.

$$(X\, f_\alpha)\,(q) = 0,\ 1 \leqslant \alpha \leqslant n{-}1,\ q \in N.$$

Therefore the space $H(N)_q$ of holomorphic tangent vectors is

$$H(N)_q = \{X = \Sigma\, a_j \frac{\partial}{\partial z_j} \mid \Sigma\, a_j \frac{\partial f_\alpha}{\partial z_j}(q) = 0,\ 1 \leqslant \alpha \leqslant n{-}1\}.$$

The dimension over **C** of this space is $\geqslant l$.

We will assume that N is *generic* in the sense that $\forall\, q \in N$

$$\dim_{C} H(N)_q = l.$$

In this case (if ω is sufficiently small) we can select along N, l vector fields $X_1, \ldots, X_l$ linearly independent over **C** at each point q and generating the space $H(N)_q$.

One realizes from the *definitions* that if $t_1, \ldots t_{n+l}$ are local coordinates near p on N every tangent vector field X is represented by a first-order homogeneous differnetial operator on N

$$X = \sum_{j=1}^{n+l} \alpha_j(t) \frac{\partial}{\partial t_j}$$

and, conversely, every operator of this type comes from a tangent vector field.

Moreover, one verifies also immediately that, if N is generic,

1) then $[X_i, X_j] = \Sigma k_{ij}^{\nu} X_\nu$ i.e. setting $\mathscr{H}(N) = \{\sum_1^l \alpha_i X_i \mid \alpha_i \in C^\infty\}$ $[\mathscr{H}(N), \mathscr{H}(N)] \subset \mathscr{H}(N)$.
2) $\mathscr{H}(N) \cap \overline{\mathscr{H}(N)} = 0$.

b) *Tangential Cauchy-Riemann complex.* On ω we can consider the Dolbeault complex

$$C^*(\omega) \equiv \{\mathscr{E}^{(0)}(\omega) \xrightarrow{\bar\partial} \mathscr{E}^{(1)}(\omega) \xrightarrow{\bar\partial} \mathscr{E}^{(2)}(\omega) \xrightarrow{\bar\partial} \ldots\}$$

where $\mathscr{E}^{(j)}(\omega)$ = space of C^∞ exterior form of type (0, j). Setting

$$\mathscr{I}^{(j)}(\omega) = \{\varphi \in \mathscr{E}^{(j)}(\omega) \mid \varphi = \sum_1^{n-1} f_\alpha \psi_\alpha + \sum_1^{n-1} \bar\partial f_\alpha \wedge \eta_\alpha, \psi_\alpha \in \mathscr{E}^{(j)}(\omega), \eta_\alpha \in H\mathscr{E}^{(j-1)}(\omega)\},$$

we get a subcomplex

$$\mathscr{I}^*(\omega) = \{\mathscr{I}^{(0)}(\omega) \xrightarrow{\bar\partial} \mathscr{I}^{(1)}(\omega) \xrightarrow{\bar\partial} \mathscr{I}^{(2)}(\omega) \xrightarrow{\bar\partial} \ldots\}$$

and thus setting $Q^{(j)}(N) = \mathscr{E}^{(j)}(\omega)/\mathscr{I}^{(j)}(\omega)$ a quotient complex on N

$$Q^*(N) = \{Q^{(0)}(N) \xrightarrow{\bar\partial_N} Q^{(1)}(N) \xrightarrow{\bar\partial_N} Q^{(2)}(N) \xrightarrow{\bar\partial_N} \ldots\}.$$

By the assumption that N is generic $\bar\partial f_1, \ldots, \bar\partial f_{n-1}$ are linearly independent at each point $q \in N$ and therefore they can be taken into a basis

$$\omega_1, \ldots, \omega_l, \bar\partial f_1, \ldots, \bar\partial f_{n-1}$$

of (0, 1) forms in ω (ω sufficiently small).

It follows then that

$$(\alpha)\ Q^{(j)}(N) = \mathscr{E}(N)^{\binom{l}{j}}$$
$$= \{ \sum_{\alpha_1 < \ldots < \alpha_j} a_{\alpha_1 \ldots \alpha_j} \omega_{\alpha_1} \wedge \ldots \wedge \omega_{\alpha_j}, a_{\alpha_1 \ldots \alpha_j} \in \mathscr{E}(N)\},$$

(β) the operators $\bar{\partial}_N$ are differential operators.
Thus the tangential complex will be

$$Q^0(N) \xrightarrow{\bar{\partial}_N} Q^1(N) \xrightarrow{\bar{\partial}_N} \ldots \xrightarrow{\bar{\partial}_N} Q^l(N) \longrightarrow 0.$$

Note that this complex no longer has constant coefficients. *In particular* $Q^0(N) = \mathscr{E}(N)$ *and for* $u \in Q^0(N)$ *the condition* $\bar{\partial}_N u = 0$ is equivalent to the linear system $\{\bar{X}_j u_{1 \leqslant j \leqslant l} = 0$. Indeed $\bar{\partial}_N u = 0$ is equivalent for any C^∞ extension $\tilde{u}$ of u to

$$(\bar{\partial}\tilde{u}_q) = 0 \bmod ((\bar{\partial}f_1), \ldots (\bar{\partial}f_{n-l})_q),$$

which means $\left(\frac{\partial \tilde{u}}{\partial \bar{z}_j}\right)_q$ are linear combinations of $\left(\frac{\partial f_\alpha}{\partial \bar{z}_j}\right)_q$.

But this can be stated by saying that whenever $\Sigma b_j \left(\frac{\partial f_\alpha}{\partial \bar{z}_j}\right)_q = 0\ \forall\ \alpha$, then

also $\Sigma b_j \left(\frac{\partial \tilde{u}}{\partial \bar{z}_j}\right)_q = 0$, i.e. $\{\bar{X}_j u_{1 \leqslant j \leqslant l} = 0$.

c) *The case of a hypersurface* $N \subset \mathbf{C}^n$. If $l = n - 1$ then $N = S$ is a hypersurface and it is automatically generic. Let us introduce into the picture the Levi form of S at p and let us assume that it has p-positive and q-negative eigenvalues at the analytic tangent space at the point $z_0 \in S$. Let U be a neighborhood of $z_0 \in S$ and let us resume the notations of the second chapter. We consider in particular the cohomology of U^+ and U^- which is, by definition, the cohomology of the complexes $C^*(U^+)$ and $C^*(U^-)$ of forms which are C^∞ up to S and with the boundary operator the operator $\bar{\partial}$.

By a theorm of regularization of J.J. Kohn and L. Nirenberg one can prove the following (see [4], [16]).

Theorem: *At any point* $z_0 \in S$ *where the Levi form on the analytic tangent space has p-positive and q-negative eigenvalues one can find a fundamental sequence of Stein neighborhoods* $\{U_\nu\}_{\nu \in \mathbf{Z}}$ *of* z_0 *such that*

$$H^s(U_\nu^+) = 0 \quad \text{if} \begin{cases} s > n - q - 1 \\ or \\ 0 < s < p \end{cases} \qquad \forall \nu \in \mathbf{Z}$$

and similarly

$$H^s(U_\nu^-) = 0 \quad \text{if} \begin{cases} s > n - p - 1 \\ \text{or} \\ 0 < s < q \end{cases} \qquad \forall\, \nu \in \mathbf{Z}.$$

Moreover if $p > 0$ *we can also assume that we have a surjective map*

$$H^0(U_\nu) \longrightarrow H^0(U_\nu^+) \longrightarrow 0$$

and if $q > 0$ *that we have a surjective map*

$$H^0(U_\nu) \longrightarrow H^0(U_\nu^-) \longrightarrow 0.$$

From the Mayer-Vietoris sequence for U_ν, as $H^j(U_\nu) = 0$ if $j > 0$, we deduce the short exact sequences

$$0 \longrightarrow H^0(U_\nu) \longrightarrow H^0(U_\nu^+) \oplus H^0(U_\nu^-) \longrightarrow H^0(S) \longrightarrow 0$$

$$H^s(U_\nu^+) \oplus H^s(U_\nu^-) \xrightarrow{\ \sim\ } H^s(S) \quad \text{if } s > 0.$$

The situation can then be illustrated as follows in the case of a nondegenerate Levi form:

Case 1 $\quad 0 < p < q = n - 1 - p$

$$\begin{array}{lllll}
U^+ & H^0(U^+) & H^p(U^+) & & \text{(the other groups are zero).} \\
 & \downarrow\wr & \downarrow\wr & & \\
S & H^0(S) & H^p(S) & H^q(S) & \\
 & \multicolumn{3}{l}{\xrightarrow{\hspace{8cm}}} & \\
 & \uparrow\wr & & \uparrow\wr & \\
U^- & H^0(U^-) & & H^q(U^+) &
\end{array}$$

Case 2 $\quad 0 < p = q = \frac{n-1}{2} \qquad$ (n odd)

$$\begin{array}{llll}
U^+ & H^0(U^+) & H^p(U^+) & \text{(the other groups are zero).} \\
 & \downarrow\wr & \downarrow & \\
S & H^0(S) & H^p(S) \simeq H^p(U^+) \oplus H^p(U^-) & \\
 & \multicolumn{2}{l}{\xrightarrow{\hspace{10cm}}} & \\
 & \uparrow\wr & \uparrow & \\
U^- & H^0(U^-) & H^p(U^-) &
\end{array}$$

By the argument used in the second chapter one can prove that for nondegenerate Levi forms one has

$$\dim_{\mathbf{C}} H^p(U^+) = \infty \text{ and } \dim_{\mathbf{C}} H^q(U^-) = \infty$$

Again by the same type of Baire category reasoning one deduces that the complex

$$Q^0(S) \xrightarrow{\bar\partial_S} Q^1(S) \xrightarrow{\bar\partial_S} \cdots \xrightarrow{\bar\partial_S} Q^{n-1}(S) \longrightarrow 0$$

fails to admit Poincaré's lemma on $Q^p(S)$ and $Q^q(S)$ at any point $z_0 \in S$.

4. Abstract Local Cauchy-Riemann Structures

a) A local abstract *Cauchy-Riemann structure of type* n, l on an open set $\Omega \subset \mathbf{R}^{n+l}$ is the assignment of a system of homogeneous linear partial differential equations of first order with C^∞ coefficients;

$$(1) \left\{ \underset{1 \leqslant j \leqslant l}{X_j u} \equiv \sum_{s=1}^{n+l} a_s^{(j)}(x) \frac{\partial u}{\partial x_s} = 0 \quad (a_s^{(j)} \in \mathscr{E}(\Omega)) \right.$$

with the following properties:

(α) The vector fields X_j are linearly independent over **C** at each point of Ω.

(β) The system (1) is in involution, i.e.

$$[X_i, X_j] = \Sigma k_{ij}^s(x) X_s \quad (k_{ij}^s \in \mathscr{E}(\Omega)).$$

(γ) The vector fields $X_1, \ldots, X_l, \bar X_1, \ldots, \bar X_l$ are linearly independent (thus $0 \leqslant l \leqslant n$) at each point of ω.

Two local structures $(X_1, \ldots, X_l)$ $(Y_1, \ldots, Y_l)$ on two open sets Ω_1, Ω_2 in $\mathbf{R}^{n+l}$ will be considered *equivalent* if there exists a diffeomorphism $\tau : \Omega_1 \longrightarrow \Omega_2$ such that

$$\tau_* X_j \in \text{space generated by } Y_1, \ldots, Y_l$$
$$\tau_*^{-1} Y_i \in \text{space generated by } X_1, \ldots, X_l.$$

If $N \simeq \Omega \subset \mathbf{R}^{n+l}$ is imbedded as a locally closed generic submanifold of $\mathbf{C}^n$, then N inherits from the tangential Cauchy-Riemann equations an abstract Cauchy-Riemann structure of type n, l.

b) Given a local abstract Cauchy-Riemann structure $\{(1)\}$, one can ask whether it can be obtained locally from an imbedding in $\mathbf{C}^n$; precisely given (1) and a point $x_0 \in \Omega$, one asks if there exists a neighborhood ω of x_0 in Ω and a locally closed imbedding $\tau : \omega \longrightarrow \mathbf{C}^n$ such that

i) $\tau(\omega)$ is a generic locally closed submanifold of $\mathbf{C}^n$

ii) $\tau_*\{(1)\}$ is the set of tangential Cauchy-Riemann equations on $\tau(\omega)$.

One has the following (see [5]).

Proposition. The necessary and sufficient condition for the structure (1) to be locally imbeddable in a neighborhood of a point $x_0 \in \Omega$ is that there exists, in some neighborhood ω of x_0, n (complex valued) solutions $u = (z_1(x), \ldots, z_n(x))$ of the equations

$$\underset{1 \leqslant j \leqslant l}{X_j u = 0}$$

such that

$$\operatorname{rank}\left(\frac{\partial(z(x))}{\partial(x)}\right)_{x_0} = n.$$

Proof. Necessity: If $\tau : \omega \longrightarrow \mathbf{C}^n$ is an imbedding, then on ω, the functions $\tau^*z_1, \ldots, \tau^*z_n$ (z_i being the holomorphic coordinates in $\mathbf{C}^n$) give solutions of (1). Moreover as $\tau(\omega)$ is generic, the condition on the rank must be satisfied. This follows from the fact if we set

$$z_i = \varphi_i(x_1, \ldots, x_{n-1}) \quad \text{and set } J = \begin{pmatrix} \partial\varphi_1/\partial x_1 \ldots \partial\varphi_1/\partial x_{n+1} \\ \cdot \quad \cdot \quad \cdot \quad \cdot \\ \partial\varphi_n/\partial x_1 \ldots \partial\varphi_n/\partial x_{n+1} \end{pmatrix}$$

a vector $y = \sum_1^n a_i \dfrac{\partial}{\partial z_i} \equiv \sum_{s=1}^{n+l} \alpha_s \dfrac{\partial}{\partial x_s}$ is holomorphic and tangent to $\tau(\omega)$ if and only if $a = J\alpha$, $\bar{J}\alpha = 0$.

Sufficiency: Let $z_i = \varphi_i(x_1, \ldots, x_{n+l})$, $1 \leqslant i \leqslant n$ be solutions of (1) satisfying the rank conditions on ω. Consider the map

$$\tau : \omega \longrightarrow \mathbf{C}^n$$

given by $x \longrightarrow (\varphi_1(x), \ldots, \varphi_n(x))$. We claim that τ is a local imbedding. Indeed it is enough to show that

$$\operatorname{rank} \frac{\partial(\varphi_1, \ldots, \varphi_n, \bar{\varphi}_1, \ldots, \bar{\varphi}_n)}{\partial(x_1, \ldots, x_{n+l})} = n + l.$$

Let $(L, \bar{L})$ denote this matrix. The columns of L form a basis of the space

$$\{\eta \in \mathbf{C}^{n+l} \,|\, A\eta = 0\} = \operatorname{Ker} A, \quad \text{where } A = (a_s^{(i)}).$$

The columns of $(L, \bar{L})$ thus form a basis of Ker A + Ker $\bar{A}$ in $\mathbf{C}^{n+l}$. Now Ker A $\cap$ Ker $\bar{A}$ = Ker $\begin{pmatrix} A \\ \bar{A} \end{pmatrix}$ and thus, by assumption (γ), has dimension $n - l$. Thus

$$\begin{aligned}\dim \operatorname{Ker} A + \dim \operatorname{Ker} \bar{A} &= \operatorname{rank}(L, \bar{L}) = \\ &= \dim \operatorname{Ker} A + \dim \operatorname{Ker} \bar{A} - \dim \operatorname{Ker} A \cap \operatorname{Ker} \bar{A} \\ &= n + n - (n - l) = n + l.\end{aligned}$$

Once this is proved it is a question of applying the criterion given before to verify that $\tau(\omega)$ is a generic submanifold of $\mathbf{C}^n$.

c) That the given system (1) admits solution other than the constants is by no means obvious.

The problem of local imbeddability has a positive answer in the following instances.

(α) The system (1) has real analytic (complex valued) coefficients.

(β) $l = n$, in this case it reduces to the Newlander-Nirenberg theorem.[1]

The proof of (α) is elementary, not so the proof of (β).

In the other cases the answer is doubtful. As example of L. Nirenberg [23] shows that for $l = 1$, $n = 3$ the answer is negative. Indeed Nirenberg's example is the data of a complex vector field X on a neighborhood of the origin in $\mathbf{R}^3$ with the property that

i) $X, \bar{X}, [X, \bar{X}]$ are linearly independent at the origin,

ii) every solution u of $Xu = 0$ in a neighborhood of the origin must be constant in some neighborhood of the origin.

Now the system $Xu = 0$ defines a Cauchy-Riemann structure in a neighborhood of the origin in $\mathbf{R}^3$ of type (2, 1).[2]

1. More generally one has a positive answer to the problem of imbedding in this particular case. The system (1) satisfies in addition to conditions (α), (β), (γ) also the condition

$$(\delta) \quad [X_j, X_k] = \Sigma c^r_{jk}(x)X_r + \Sigma d^s_{jk}\bar{X}_s \quad c^r_{jk}, d^s_{jk} \in \mathscr{E}(\Omega).$$

See [22].

2. Counterexamples in higher dimension can be constructed on $\mathbf{R}^3 \times \mathbf{C}^n$ taking on $\mathbf{R}^3$ the equation of Nirenberg and on $\mathbf{C}^n$ the Cauchy-Riemann equations.

Bibliography

1. A. Andreotti. Boundary value problems and Mayer-Vietoris sequence. *Rendiconti Seminario Matermatico di Milano* **43** (1973), pp. 27–34.
2. A. Andreotti and H. Grauert. Théorèmes de finitude pour la cohomologie des espaces complexes. *Bull. Soc. Math. France* **90** (1962), pp. 193–259.
3. A. Andreotti and T. Frankel. The Lefschetz theorem on hyperplane sections. *Ann. Math.* **69** (1953), pp. 713–17.
4. A. Andreotti and C.D. Hill. E.E. Levi convexity and Hans Lewy problems, Parts I and II. *Ann. Sc. Nor. Sup. Pisa* **26** (1972), pp. 325–63, 767–806.
5. A. Andreotti and C.D. Hill. Complex characteristic coordinates and tangential Cauchy-Riemann equations. *Ann. Sc. Nor. Sup. Pisa* **26** (1972), pp. 299–324.
6. J.E. Björk. The global dimension of some algebras of differential operators. *Inventiones Math.* **17** (1972), pp. 67–68.
7. S. Bochner. Analytic and meromorphic continuation by means of Green's formula. *Ann. Math.* **44** (1963), pp. 652–73.
8. S. Bochner and W.T. Martin. Functions of several complex variables. Princeton Univ. Press, Princeton, 1968.
9. H. Cartan. Séminaire Ecole Normale Supérieure 1951–52.
10. G. Fichera. Caratterinazione della traccia sulla frontiera di un campo d'una funzione analitica di più variabili complesse. *Atti Ac. Naz. Lincei, Rend.* **22** (1957) pp. 706–15.
11. H. Grauert. On Levi's problem and the imbedding of real analytic manifolds. *Ann. Math.* **58** (1958), pp. 460–72.
12. T. Hadamard. *Leçons sur le calcul des variations*, Vol. I., Paris 1910.
13. H. Hopf. *Lectures on differential Geometry*, Stanford Univ. (Mimeo. notes), 1951?
14. L. Hörmander. *An Introduction to Complex Analysis in Several Variables.* Van Nostrand, Princeton, 1966.
15. L. Hörmander. L^2 estimates and existence theorems for the $\bar{\partial}$-operator. *Acta Math.* **113** (1965), pp. 89–152.
16. J.J. Kohn and L. Nirenberg. Non coercive boundary value problems. *Comm. Pure Appl. Math.* **18** (1965), pp. 643–92.
17. E.E. Levi. Studii sur punti singolari essenziali delle funzioni analitiche di due o più variabili complesse. *Opere* Cremonese, Roma (1958), pp. 187–213.
18. H. Lewy. An example of a smooth linear partial differential equation without solution. *Ann. Math.* **66** (1957), pp. 155–58.

19. F.S. Macaulay. *The Algebraic Theory of Modular Systems.* Cambridge Univ. Press, 1916.
20. B. Malgrange. Division des distributions. Séminaire Schwartz, 1959–60.
21. E. Martinelli. Sopra un Teorema di F. Severi nella teoria delle funzioni di piu variabili complesse. *Rend Mat. Appl.* **20** (1961), pp. 81–96.
22. L. Nirenberg. *Complex Frobenius Theorem.* Seminar on Analytic Functions, Institute for Advanced Study, Princeton (1951), pp. 172–89.
23. L. Nirenberg. On a question of Hans Lewy. To appear.
24. V.P. Palamodov. *Linear Differential Operators with Constant Coefficients.* Springer Berlin, 1970.
25. J.P. Serre. Quelques problémes globaux relatifs aux variété de Stein. *Colloque sur les fonctions de plusieurs variables complexes*, Brussels, 1953, pp. 57–68.